Memoirs of a Hi-Tech Hustler

Second Edition

By Gregory D. Evans

A <u>Global</u> <u>Technology</u> <u>Publishing</u> book

The Cyber Group Network Corporation website: www.cybergroupnetwork.com

<u>Written by</u>: Gregory D. Evans

<u>Contributing Authors</u>: Knightmare, DG, King Knox, Executive Image, Kevin Mic, Dr. Hackafellow, & Megahertz

<u>Editor</u>: Craig W. Elliott

<u>Publicist</u>: PC Public Relations (323) 993-0773

<u>Front and Back Cover</u>: Dan Chapman (323) 906-8541

<u>Cover Layout</u>: Kat Trevino

<u>Page Layout</u>: Kat Trevino

Email: Katt@cgpn.net

Hi-Tech Hustler Scrapbook Chapter is copy written by one of the following publications: Rolling Stone, Los Angeles Times, Vibe Magazine, The Sun Newspaper, The Business Press, & Global Technology Publishing.

A <u>Global Technology Publishing</u> book

Table Of Contents

Acknowledgements

Thanks

I would like to thank a few people who have helped me rebuild my empire. The Evans and Van Meter Family, Jesus Bernal, Damone Schraier, Dal Hanseth, The Webley Family, Tom Meeks, Tony Miller, Dion Davis, Roy Mason, Bruce Bell, Gready Herrel, Phyllis Caddell, to my Cyber Group Family, and to all of our shareholders. Special thanks to Angela Davis; you did not have to do what you did. And a very special "Thank you very much" to Gregory and Marquis'.

Special Thanks

I was driving my new Mercedes SL 500 with the top down on the corner of Court and North E. St. in San Bernardino, California. As I was sitting at the light bobbing my head to ICE Cube, I noticed an unmarked police car pull up next to me. I turned my head really slow to look at them as they were already staring at me. I noticed that the cop in the passenger seat was DICKtective Rocha, the same DICKtective that arrested me on the same corner 21 months earlier. I looked him in his eyes as he looked at me with a puzzling look on his face as if he was wondering what I was doing out of jail. I cracked a smile, lifted my left arm displaying my new $60,000 dollar Rolex, gave him the middle finger, and drove off. I remember the day he put handcuffs on me, he said "Your'e going up the river." I guess he thought I was going "up the river" to drown. Little did he know I was on the swim team. I held my breath for every bit of 16 months, 6 days, and 55 minutes.

Even though DICKtective Rocha is an overweight, badly dressed, lying, crooked (Should have worked out of Rampart), bad breathed, wannabee FBI agent who probably couldn't make the weight requirement without Jenny Craig's help, I would not be making millions off this book if it weren't for him. So lets look at all of DICKtective Rocha's hard work: He arrested me and in less than 2 years later I'm richer than I ever was before. And he's still a fourth rate DICKtective. It's funny how things work out. To DICK-tective Rocha: Thanks for all the money you have inspired me to make.

Preface

Who say's crime doesn't pay? Ford Motors makes 100's of millions of dollars every year selling police cars to law enforcement. What about the companies who make police uniforms and bullet proof vests? Should I even mention criminal defense attorneys? What about the company's who build prisons? There are more prisons being built than there are high schools.

And then there is the technology business. If it weren't for Hi-Tech Hustlers writing viruses there would be no Mcafee or Norton Anti-Virus software. Both of which make ten's of millions of dollars every year selling anti-virus software. Then there are the companies who write and build computer firewalls and hacker traps. Let's not forget Hollywood who glorifies Hi-Tech Computer Nerds in movies.

Hi-Tech Hustlers have been around since technology has been around: From the day when Ben Franklin discovered electricity to the day the first radar systems were developed. It's important to know that the more advanced society becomes, the less 'common criminals' you will see. You will see a lot more Hi-Tech Hustlers.

The stories you are about to read may or may not be true. I will let you make your own judgment on which stories are real or not. I think you can understand that it would be ludicrous to commit a crime and then detail it in a book with who, what, when, where, and how you did it. So the names, places, and dates, have been changed to protect the guilty. Just keep in mind, if I wrote a story about the CIA selling drugs in South Central Los Angeles to finance a war in Central America 7 years ago, would you have believed it? Probably not, but didn't it happen? The stories do not necessarily reflect the life of one or more individuals, but are a conglomeration of stories of several individuals rolled into one character. Please do not try to recreate any actions in this book. This book is for entertainment purposes only. Now with that disclaimer in mind, welcome to the mind of a Hi-Tech Hustler.

In The Beginning...

7

As far back as I can recall I have always had a deep interest and curiosity in how mechanical things work. Ever since I learned to walk I was tearing my toys apart to locate the internal working parts. Trying, often unsuccessfully, to put them back together again.

I remember one day in particular when I was six years old. I was watching the "Little Rascals" on our slightly out of focus television. The wide-eyed innocence of a first grader, I watched anxiously as Spanky and Alfalfa modified two tin cans with a long string into a primitive telephone. It seemed simple enough to make. I knew where to find the string and all I would have to come up with were the two tin cans. I coerced my mom into serving canned peas for dinner. Knowing the cans had to be identically sized cans, I requested extra portions. Incidentally, I hadn't counted on her making me clean my plate and finish the rest of the peas in the pot, which was unfortunate since I never much cared for canned peas. After trying to choke them down for some time, I started spreading the mushy green balls around my plate and spitting the rest into my napkin.

What seemed like hours later, my mother finally excused me from the table. I grabbed the prized cans out of the trash and gave them a quick rinse. Then I dashed to the bedroom I shared with my little brother. With some degree of difficulty, I managed to poke two holes in the bottom of each can with a screwdriver. Next, I began inserting and securing the ends of a lengthy piece of string to each can. I recruited my mother to recite the alphabet from her bedroom, speaking into the can as I listened in my room on the other can. I thought to myself, "Why doesn't it work like it did for Spanky and Alfalfa?" My heart sank and my stomach churned when I thought about all those damn peas I had to eat. To this day I can't stomach canned peas.

The disappointment was only momentary however, as my curiosity continued to evolve. In an effort to figure out why my canned telephones didn't work, I decided to disassemble the kitchen wall phone and hopefully discover the difference in the phone systems. That was a big mistake. It earned me one hell of an ass whooping from my mother. She gave me one of them good old fashion "You just shot Malcolm X" ass whoopings! It was one of the many beatings I took over the years for my many attempts at technological discovery. The worst one came from my father. He put the fear of God in me! When I was bad, he used to break my ass off like a Kit Kat! I don't know if it was the cold glare he had in his eyes, or the right crosses to the jaw that hurt worse.

It was out of fear of letting my father down and also the ultimate physical pain that he would deliver to my butt that started me on the road to deceit and lying. Don't misunderstand me. I blame no one except myself for the choices I have made that landed me in jail. I am only attempting to explain the circumstances for my choices.

The next few years of my life are inconsequential in the telling of my life story. What is important is my first introduction to the computer in the seventh grade at Annapolis Junior High School. It was a Tandy TSR-80, and I experienced love at first sight. I was like a virgin with an older more experienced woman. But I still got hooked. I spent all my free time in the computer lab learning everything I could about my new lover. Including her likes, dislikes, and how to caress her keys to reach mutual satisfaction. She turned into my hoe and I was her pimp.

Our final exam for the semester was to create an accounting program for home. As others in my class struggled with the assignment, I found it to be almost second nature. The program earned me an 'A', not to mention the respect of my fellow classmates and teacher.

I too was proud of my conquest over the machine. I was so proud in fact that I decided to approach Jim, the biggest drug dealer in our projects, with a business proposal.

Jim lived down a block or so from the neighborhood where I was brought up. His third floor flat had people coming and going at all times of the day and night. There was always a group of three or four homeboys just hanging out on the front stoop. They were keeping an eye out for narcs, vice, or anyone that could be a threat to Jim and his organization. No one got in to see Jim unless the guys in the front cleared them. I was cleared for entrance because I hung with one of the so-called "Soldiers" little brothers.

I found Jim kickin'-it on the couch with three of his soldiers in adjacent chairs, drinking a can of Pepsi, and his phone was within comfortable reach. Jim had a certain presence about him. He wore a purple and gold jogging suit, laden with heavy gold chains and rings. Only someone of his formidable stature could carry all that weight in gold. Standing in the doorway of his flat, Jim spoke first, "Come on in kid, what's up?" On that cue, I began to explain to Jim about my accounting program and what it could do for him and his organization. I told him that for $20 dollars a day, I could do a program that would enable him to keep track of all his soldiers and employees. He could track who has drugs, who owes, and who's been fronted by way of a daily profit and loss statement. With an inaudible grunt, and a handshake, a mutual deal was struck.

The next day I went to the computer room after school and started working on Jim's program. According to the information Jim gave me the day before, he was making an average of $16,000 dollars a day, but only paying me $20 dollars to keep track of his illegal merchandise. It was a good deal for Jim. After tallying his profits on the school computer, or shall I say my hoe, I would drop them off at Jim's on my way home for dinner and collect my twenty. Easy money!

After about one week, I started to notice that one of his soldiers named Mo, a.k.a. Maurice, was skimming about $600 dollars a day from Jim. I knew what this sort of information would mean. Jim was a generous and decent guy as far as drug dealers go. He was a family man with three kids, and everyone shared a part in his lucrative drug trafficking, but he was not a man to be fucked with.

That evening, I reported to Jim as usual. As Jim glanced at his daily balance sheet I could see the veins in his neck starting to bulge. "Hey kid, what the fuck does this mean?" I explained the best I could about the unevenness of the balance sheet, then got my twenty, and headed for the door. As I was hurrying down the hallway, I could hear Jim yelling to one of his soldiers, "I want that motha-fucking Mo, dragged here by his balls. Nobody steals from me!"

The next day at school, I began to notice that girls and the older guys were acknowledging me in ways they hadn't before. I had no idea what was different about today versus any other day. It wasn't until homeroom when my cousin came in and asked, "What the hell did you do?" Then I realized what warranted all the extra attention. Defensively I replied, "I didn't do shit." He then said, "Well word has it you're Jim's right hand man. And if anyone fucks with you he'll kill them and their dog too." I thought, "Oh Shit, that's all I need, for my ego to get even bigger than the projects themselves."

At my next drop off at Jim's, I was greeted with props (handshakes) and he gave me a raise to $100 dollars per day. It only seemed fair since I had just saved his ass from losing six hundred dollars a day from Mo. I could hardly believe it myself. Here I was running a $480,000 dollar a month business on the school's computer, suspected by no one.

I was so caught up in running Jim's balance sheets, and moving up in Jim's world, that I began to neglect my own schoolwork. My grades began to drop and I was failing most of my subjects. Progress reports were due out soon but there was no way in hell I could let my father find out I was failing most of my classes, with the exception of computer class of course. I was panic stricken the day the reports were to go out. Then I figured out that I could duplicate them on my computer, and so I changed my grades into ones that my father would be proud of and exemplify just how brainy I was. The only problem was that my computer teacher was sick that day and there would be no after school computer lab. Luckily, however, I had a sixth period computer class that afternoon. I was able to leave a window slightly ajar. The window opened vertically so it was nearly impossible to notice it was open. Later that evening, I gave my parents some lame excuse and went back to school. I climbed in through the open window undetected. It didn't take me long to boot the TSR-80, and I was in business.

The progress reports were printed on regular white computer paper, with just the name and address of the school centered on top. Just below and to the left of the schools address I typed in my full name and student identification number. I then began to list all of my classes and fill in the grades: A's, B's, and for added effect, an occasional C. At the bottom of the page, I added the spot for the parent's signature, and then printed the report out. It took me less than thirty minutes to duplicate the whole thing. I laid the fake and the original side by side, on the desk. It was a perfect forgery. Showing it to my father would mark the essential moment of truth.

My dad didn't get home from his second job until 11:20pm. He plopped down in his recliner in front of the television to catch the last of the late night news. I handed him my progress report and quickly retreated to the safety of the bathroom. After what seemed like hours, I heard him calling me. As I left the bathroom, he was standing in the hallway, seemingly blocking any possible escape route. "Come here boy," he said emotionlessly. I immediately broke into a cold sweat and began to brace myself for the incoming right cross to the jaw. As I approached him, I saw his arm rise, and I just knew I was about to be brought to my death. Suddenly, he grabbed me and gave me a big hug and said, "I'm so proud of you. I knew you had it in you." Yes, it worked!

From that day forward, I continued the forgeries for my parents. I also began to sell personalized progress reports for fellow classmates for $20 dollars a pop. I processed over two hundred progress reports in the upcoming quarters.

It was the day after progress reports came out. Jim showed up after school in a new jet black BMW. You couldn't help but notice him. All the junior high girls swarmed around Jim, admiring their reflections in the shine of the finish. "Yo Kid, jump in!" Jim commanded. I immediately complied, knowing no one said "no" to Jim. Jim was like God. I felt like one of the chosen few. As we drove through the hood people waived, kids ran up to the car, and passing cars honked as we passed. Seeing people's reactions to Jim's new car, you would have thought Michael Jackson himself was behind the wheel.

Jim told me he had been out shopping for a birthday present for his youngest son, and decided to get a little something for himself also. Just riding in the Beamer made me feel like we were the center of attention. And we were! I said to Jim, "Look at all these motha-fucka's tripping, they love us." "Listen little brotha," Jim replied, "These motha-fucka's don't love us. They're in love with the money we make. When the money stops, so does the admiration. If we disappeared today there would be at least fifty more people standing in line to take our place before our bodies even got cold. You're a smart kid, too smart to get caught up in all this shit." Jim was about to give me a lesson in life that I carry with me even to this very day: "Just remember kid," he said, "There are two types of people in this fucked up world - pimps and hoes." I glanced back over to him with a look like he was spaced out on acid or something. He met my glance, and continued. "I'm not trying to be funny," he continued, "In this world the hoes make the real money, busting their asses, and then what do they do? They bring the dough back to their pimps. I'm not talking about the pimps and hoes you know in the ghetto. I'm talking about the pimps and hoes in the white man's world. For example, if they can get away with paying a basketball player a million dollars or so, how much do you think he's making for the owners of the team? The same goes for my business. If I pay someone a grand to sell my drugs, you better believe I'm making at least two grand off his ass."

When I look back on our conversation, and from what I know today, I know he was absolutely right. Looking at some of the notable people in the media, I can categorize them into one of those two groups - pimps or hoes. Bill Gates, I would consider a pimp; Snoop Doggy Dog, a hoe; Sean Puffy Combs, a pimp; Madonna, a pimp; Johnny Cochran, a pimp; Oprah Winfrey, a pimp; President Clinton is both a pimp and a hoe; and Monica Lewinski is definitely a hoe.

As Jim and I drew close to my house, I had Jim drop me off about a block away. I didn't want my parents seeing me hanging with him. As I was about to get out, he put his hand on my shoulder and said something I had never heard him say before. He said, "I love ya kid, and you remember what I told you, and the world is yours. Now get the hell out of here and let me get to my kid's birthday party." I gave him a pound (handshake) and got out.

As I headed home, I saw Jim turn left onto the next avenue. I hadn't gone more than fifty feet when I heard a hail of gunfire from the avenue. It sounded like the finale at the Fourth of July fireworks. I stopped dead in my tracks. I had no idea where the shots were coming from until I heard someone running by mumbling, "they shot his fucking ass, they shot Jim." I started running in the direction of the avenue that they had come from. I ran faster than I had ever run in my life. As I got closer I heard a car horn sounding, and it got louder the closer I got to the corner of the avenue. As I rounded the corner onto the avenue, I saw Jim's bullet ridden car. Jim's body was slumped over the steering wheel. I was about twenty yards away and I stopped again to try and comprehend what had just happened. The back window of the BMW was shattered and there must have been a hundred rounds of ammunition emptied into the car. Then I witnessed something that might have made me commit my first murder. There was Jim in his silk Puma jogging suit covered with blood. And out of the corner of my eye, I noticed one of Jim's homies run to the car, open the door, then drag his limp body out. He laid Jim on the pavement next to the driver's door. At first I thought he was there to see if Jim was still alive or to resuscitate him. Then I saw him rummaging through the pockets of Jim's jogging suit. I stood frozen in disbelief. He was robbing a dead man. Seconds later, several others ran to Jim's bloody body and started removing his Rolex, chains, rings, and even his shoes. I don't know where I summoned the nerve, but I ran to the car and with a Bruce Lee type of flying kick, I nailed the guy that had dragged Jim's body out onto the street. I then proceeded to kick his motha-fucking ass. I then reached into the car and grabbed a semi automatic pistol from under the front seat. I knew Jim never went anywhere without his piece loaded and ready to go. I began firing into the air, mostly out of rage, until I had emptied the clip. Once the shots started ringing out the vultures cleared the street. With tears rolling down my face, I sat next to Jim on the cold pavement - still grasping the emptied pistol between my legs. Through my tears I could see the wrapped birthday present in the back seat. It was covered with shards of broken glass and filled with bullet holes. Who could have set up such an ambush, and why? I didn't find out the answers until sometime later. The word on the street was that Jim was murdered by his half brother. He had driven down from Baltimore to get revenge for Jim not allowing him to deal heroin in his territory.

The following week, I attended Jim's funeral. The casket remained closed because the top of his head was pretty much blown off in the ambush. There were only a handful of people in attendance outside of his immediate family. As I sat in the quiet church, starring at the casket, I reflected on the conversation Jim and I had right before he died. Then I wondered where were all his so-called friends and followers? He was right. They didn't love him, only his money. The old adage was true. "Money can't buy you everything."

That day I made a vow to myself to never use or sell drugs. I wouldn't want my family to have to sit through a closed casket funeral for me.

I love you Jim, You taught me so much in such a short time, and I'll never forget you. Rest in Peace man.

My First Real Job Experience

My senior year in high school I got in contact with a girl I had dated in sixth grade. We had a long distance relationship my entire senior year. I flew her from California to Bedford, Massachusetts for my prom. I thought I was so in love that I decided to bypass college and head to California to be with her. Besides, I thought that if I start my own business right out of high school, all of the kids I would have been graduating with in college would be applying for jobs with my company. Instead of my competing with them at IBM, I'd be their boss. With that logic in mind, three days after graduating from high school I had fifty dollars in my pocket and a plane ticket. About a month later, after landing in California, I landed a job with ComputerLand located in Victorville California. I loved my job! I was selling computers to the Naval Weapons Center in China Lake and the school districts in Victorville, Apple Valley, and Hesperia. I even sold computers to the police department and NASA at Edwards Air Force Base. There were about twenty employees at Computerland. Of the twenty employees only two were Black. One was, possibly the best computer technician in the world, named Mike, and myself in sales. Although there were not many minorities, we were all a happy family. I owe a lot to them because they sent me to schools to get the training I needed to go out on my own. I went to Apple Certification School, Novel, Microsoft, IBM, Compaq, AST, and many others.

When I was younger I lived in Victorville, California for about two years. I was in the sixth grade and I attended Park View Elementary School. This is the same school that would change my life ten years later. One day while I was working for ComputerLand, I was sent out to Park View Elementary School to deliver some computers. I met a third grade teacher I will call "Ms. Smith." She was around twenty-three years old and about five feet six inches tall. She had a nice figure and she was White. I haven't, to this day, ever dated a White woman. It's not because I don't find them attractive, because I do. I just love Black women a lot more. I also had never been put in the situation to date outside my race. I would make deliveries and show some new products off to the school where she worked. This was part of my job at Computerland. She and I would sit and talk about school, computers, politics, or nothing in particular. One day when I was at the school, Ms. Smith asked me if I watched the Arsenio Hall Show. I told her every night. The Arsenio Hall Show was the hottest thing on TV at the time. After talking about the show, she said she could get us some tickets and she asked me if I wanted to go. I knew then that she wanted more than a professional relationship. Although I know there are probably a thousand men who would have jumped at the opportunity, I didn't feel comfortable for two reasons. The first being that my first son was about to be born in two to three weeks by a woman I was very much in love with. The second reason was that I couldn't see myself dating a White woman. Not that I have a problem with people dating outside their race. I just didn't want to be that stereotypical Black man that gets a little bit of money in his pocket and thinks that dating a Black women is beneath him. About a week later I was in the store after hours talking to my manager David. We weren't talking about much. David had his feet up on the desk and I was slouched down in a chair a little. The phone rang. David answered and told me it was "Ms. Smith" and she wanted to talk to me. He handed me the phone and leaned back in his chair and smiled. I said, "Hello this is Greg can I help you." She said, "Hello Greg. I wanted to know if you played tennis?" I told her yes, just a little. She then asked if I wanted to go out and play tennis that weekend. I told her no because I had a previous arrangement. She was cool with that and she said, "O.k., maybe some other time." We ended the conversation and I looked at David as I hung up the phone. He was just smiling from ear to ear. I told David, the manager and my so-called friend, about her asking me to go see the Arsenio Hall Show. He said, "She probably likes you and that's good. She'll probably order more computers." The very next day my girlfriend was in the store waiting for me to take her to lunch. Another teacher from Park View Elementary School walked in and saw my girlfriend and I together. The teacher asked another employee who the pregnant woman was with Greg? The employee told her that the pregnant woman was my girlfriend. When the teacher returned to school that day she told Ms. Smith that she saw me with my pregnant girlfriend. I guess the two of them were so upset about the fact that I had a girlfriend that they came up with a bullshit story. About a week later (And a week before my son was to be born) I was closing up the store when David called me into his office. When I went in the office David was behind his desk, and one of the owners, Carolyn, sitting in the chair next to him. I took a seat and said, "What's up? Am I getting a bonus or something?" I was their top employee. David said, "Ms. Smith called today and said you were at Park View Elementary School flirting with her. She said you asked her to go and see the Arsenio Hall Show and to play tennis with her. What do you have to say for yourself?" I said, "She's full of shit. David you answered the phone when she called. You sat in that same seat and listened to the conversation I had with her. I told you how she asked me out. You said, 'she probably likes you and that's good sales'." Carolyn stopped me and said, "Well Greg, we can't have a scandal like this, so we are going to let you go." I looked at both of them in their eyes. I had a tear that was about to form in my eye. I said, "All the money I made for you. Working overtime without asking for extra pay. I never once caused any problems for you or your store. Just because someone said I did something I didn't do, you're firing me. A week before my son will be born, and two weeks before Christmas?" I continued, "David, you just gave a speech to us about how we are all family and should be able to depend on each other here at the store. Let me ask you if that teacher were Black and she said I had flirted with her, would I still be fired?" No one said anything. They handed me my final paycheck and a box with all my personal stuff. I knew when I saw the box of my things packed that they had planned on firing me no matter what I did. That was my first lesson about the real world. You can work with White people, you can help them make money, and you can even live in their neighborhood. But whatever you do, don't mess with their women.

About a week later I was recruited by Sears Business Center in San Bernardino. I knew I was in demand. Sears Business Center was a division of the Sears Corporation that sold computers to major corporations. I worked there for three months before the company had a budget problem and cut jobs. The day I got laid off was the day I decided that I would never work for anyone else again. Never! To this day I never have.

The $500 Million Digital Takeover

A few years back when cellular phones first started becoming accessible to the general public, it seemed like just another gadget most people could live without. It didn't take long for cell phones to quickly become an item that people looked upon as a necessity, and not just one of convenience or luxury. Business could be conducted on busy freeways, or waiting in line. Work was no longer just in the confines of the office. The cell phone freed up Americans like nothing else had since the production of cars in the early twentieth century. Women no longer needed to fear driving alone at night. Help was always just a call away. No more waiting at home for the phone to ring.

The popularity of the cell phone boomed almost over night, and so did the illegal cloning of analog cell phones. This is where I came in. If there was an easier and quicker way for money to be made in a new developing technical field - I had my finger in it.

Let me start off by asking if you have ever had your analog phone cloned and you never understood how it happened? There's a good probability I was behind those enormous phone bills you got on your cloned phone before you finally switched to a digital phone.

Don't hate me yet! I was just the facilitator. The real masterminds behind the cloning were some of the digital phone manufacturers and cellular service providers themselves. Incredulous as it may seem, corporate America does create and sponsor illegal activities for monetary gain.

The story I am about to relay to you may seem unbelievable to most of you who trust in the ethics of free enterprise and the American way. Let me assure you the tale I'm about to weave is true. Some of the names have been changed to protect others, but mostly to protect me. With that disclaimer in mind, let me begin.

First of all, I want to briefly discuss the difference between analog and digital phones. Analog lines are similar to the telephone lines in your home, in that you have just one telephone service per line. Digital lines on the other hand can handle multiple lines at the same time through just one telephone line. With digital, you can receive and place calls simultaneously. The advantages of digital over analog phones are numerous. Digital lines are cheaper for companies to supply to the consumer and even cheaper to use, although the initial investment for a digital phone is considerably more than an analog cell phone. Digital cell phones do not have static, and the reception is much clearer. Features such as caller ID, call waiting, three-way calling, numeric or alpha paging, and the capability to receive E-mail are all available on digital phones. The single biggest selling point of digital phones is their inability to be illegally cloned as easily as analog.

The ease of cell phone cloning was immediately alluring to me for its lucrative potential. Moreover, the risk factors in getting caught were relatively low, especially if I hired a couple of flunkies to be my henchmen. Allowing me to run the operation from a safe distance.

I started my business about nine years ago, with the purchase of an *Electronic Serial Number Reader,* commonly referred to as an ESN. At the time it was necessary to have an FCC license to purchase one, but that's a whole other story. ESN readers are as common as a 'black box' on airplanes. They're about the size of a standard VCR with a small screen. The purpose of an ESN reader is to capture a cellular phone's individual identity such as the area code and phone number of the phone. Every analog phone has a unique ESN that is particular to that phone. Just like a Social Security Number is unique to its holder. As long as the phone is on it will transmit a particular ESN whether you're using the phone at the time or not. If you are using your phone, the reader can still capture the ESN while also allowing the operator to listen in on your conversation up to one mile away. This device can also store up to 150 numbers in its memory and even print out the information through serial printer connections. The road map had been laid out and all I had to do was to see where it would lead me.

Louie was an acquaintance I met through a common friend when I first relocated to Southern California. Back then; Louie wasn't much more than your common street hustler with some minor financial backing from God knows where. He now owned a couple of pager and cell phone stores in the South Central area of Los Angeles. Because Louie lacked the good credit and the substantial cash deposits required to establish a legitimate business, he got into the cloning business. Likewise, his customers also had problems getting cell phones without the huge deposit and near perfect credit required by the cell phone companies. Louie's standard for credit from his customers was cash. With no credit requirements Louie was selling more phones and cloning more numbers than he could keep up with. He supplied everyone from drug dealers in Compton, to doctors in Bel Air. Louie's only problem was that he couldn't adequately supply his overwhelming demand.

I don't recall exactly how Louie and I got in to business together. I don't remember if he might have contacted me or maybe I solicited him. With my new ESN reader I began supplying Louie with ESN numbers at the cost of $60 dollars for each number.

It wasn't long before his demand exceeded 200 numbers a day, which he sold for $150 dollars per phone with a guarantee would stay on for at least 30 days. After the 30-day period, his customers would simply purchase another number. This created an abundant amount of business for Louie.

I became so busy trying to supply numbers to meet his demands that I was forced to expand my business and hire more people to acquire ESN numbers for me.

CC was a bright, middle aged, Black man, collecting disability for a work related back injury. He was looking for something on the side and he was not above cloning phones to supplement his family's income. Carlos, a young, energetic, Hispanic man, just wanted the money to get a pearl paint job on his prized 1963 Chevy Impala. The common denominator between them was money.

Carlos and CC would drive the main arteries of the California freeway system at all times of the day and night collecting numbers from the ESN. They would cover a territory from Barstow down to San Bernardino, then on to Orange County and up to Los Angeles, and occasionally even to Bakersfield. If there was traffic on any Southern California Freeway, and there usually was, you could find CC and Carlos collecting numbers as fast as they could record them.

I paid CC and Carlos $10 dollars for every number they were able to capture. It wasn't unusual for them to gather one hundred numbers a day. Not a bad day's work for just driving around, listening to tunes, and copying down numbers. Two months after entering into my arrangement with Louie, I was clearing nearly $10 thousand dollars a day. Business was good and it was about to get even better.

On one of those stifling hot smoggy days, that Southern California is so infamous for, CC and Carlos pulled off the 405 freeway to get some gas. Unfortunately, CC and Carlos found themselves near Newport Beach with no gas station in sight. They were running on fumes. As they headed west towards the coast the car sputtered and finally choked, coasting to a stop in front of an affluent gated community by the Dunes. Before they were able to exit the car, a Black and White police cruiser pulled in behind them. With lights flashing, the police operated under the guise of assisting a stranded motorist. The officers completed the formalities of checking Carlos's license and registration, while visually scanning the interior of the car and it's occupants.

This wasn't the first time CC and Carlos encountered this routine. After all, they were two minorities driving around in a rich and predominantly white part of town. It had happened before, just a different time and a different day.

After glancing at the ESN, and a couple of duffel bags in the back seat, Officer Miller asked if he could search the car. CC leaned over Carlos and said, somewhat belligerently, "How come? We weren't breaking no law, we just ran out of gas." The officer responded, "Well, if you haven't broken any laws, what's the big deal if I search the car?" Then he added, "Even if you refuse I'm going to search the car anyway."

Before CC could respond, he noticed Officer Miller unhooking the strap from around his 9mm handgun, while his partner moved from behind the car around to the passenger's side. "I guess this means you're going to search the car," replied CC. The officer retorted, "Not only am I going to search the car, but you two are going to lay down right here in the dirt, spread eagle, and watch me do it."

About this time a second patrol car arrived, and the officer got out with his pistol drawn and aimed it at CC and Carlos. Carlos figured they should comply because it would be cheaper to have the dirt cleaned from his new silk jacket, than to have a bullet hole repaired in it. So CC and Carlos assumed the position in the dirt next to the curb.

The first set of officers began searching the car not once, not twice, but three times. They looked beneath the seats, in the glove box, in the trunk, and even under the hood. They still couldn't find anything they could arrest CC and Carlos for.

During the entire search, the ESN reader remained on the back seat within clear view. Finally, the officer picked up the ESN reader in order to remove the back seat. They still had no clue what the black box really was. After what seamed like an eternity, Officer Miller, unable to locate any contraband, turned his attention to the ESN.

As luck would have it, just as Officer Miller was asking CC what the black box was used for, his cell phone began to ring in the patrol car. Officer Miller answered his phone and immediately heard his voice being repeated over the ESN - word for word. Not only was his conversation coming out of the box verbatim, but his cell phone number and ESN number appeared on the small screen of the ESN reader. By the look on his face and the motion of his lips saying "What the fuck", you would have thought Officer Miller had just won the lottery. With a Cheshire grin, Miller ordered the other officers to "Cuff'em and read them their rights." He knew he had all he needed to take CC and Carlos in.

At the station, CC was eventually allowed his one phone call and he used it to contact me. Fortunately, I had a friend in the bail bonds business that was able to post their bail. He would have them out in less than six hours, and without involving me at all. Included in my instructions to the bondsman was to pick them up and meet me at a prearranged hotel bar. I didn't want to meet with them at my office or at home, just in case the cops or District Attorney was tailing them.

I was seated in a tall red circular type booth in the dark bar when CC, Carlos, and my friend the bondsman arrived. CC greeted me with a hug, and then threw his tattered silk jacket on the booth next to me. He said, "Hey, you owe me a new jacket asshole." He then began recreating the day's events, laughing about the look on Officer Miller's face when he heard his voice come back through the ESN.

While we continued to relive the whole search and seizure that took place earlier in the day, we were interrupted by a figure emerging out of the darkness approaching our table. He was a short, balding, overweight White man, who introduced himself as "Mr. Smith." As if that wasn't suspicious enough, he was wearing a checkered sports coat that was obviously too small to button and a light green pair of pants. To top things off, I noticed on his wrist he was wearing a cheap Mickey Mouse watch. It was the kind of watch a kid would wear. This guy made the proverbial used car salesman seem well dressed.

Mr. Smith asked if he could speak to me privately for a few minutes. I debated whether talking to this guy would even be worth my while. Fortunately, I agreed to give him fifteen minutes. After all, my first impression was the oddity in which he dressed had caught my attention. Little did I know that this was about to be the most lucrative fifteen minutes of my life.

I signaled CC to pat Mr. Smith down in case he was wired or carrying a piece. I then instructed CC and Carlos to wait for me by the bar. Mr. Smith slid into the far side of the booth, and then inched his way around towards me. This was getting a little strange. I offered Mr. Smith a drink, and he declined.

Mr. Smith began the conversation by stating he represented several cellular phone companies and a few North American cell phone manufacturers. My immediate thoughts flashed back on the days events and I figured if this guy was real, he was probably just concerned with where I had gotten the ESN reader. At the time, I did not really believe he was who he represented himself to be. So I inquired further, "Just what capacity do you represent these companies in?" Mr. Smith replied, "Head of security." It figured, he did dress like an ex-cop.

What came next took me totally by surprise. Mr. Smith asked me if I would be interested in becoming a so-called silent partner with the companies he represented. I was so stunned by what I had just heard that I asked him to repeat the offer to me again. Still it took a few seconds to sink in. Well, the silent part I could comprehend; but why would some of America's largest cellular phone companies want me as a partner in any capacity, even a silent partner? Okay, so now he has my full attention and I'm on the edge of my seat. What does he really want?

Mr. Smith continued to explain that his companies had just come out with a new digital phone network that they perceived would eventually replace the current analog network. The problem was that their present customers had already made the initial investment in their analog phones. The newer digital phones could cost upwards of $1,000 dollars, and their customers were reluctant to make the switch. I interrupted, "So, where do I come in?" Mr. Smith lowered his voice a notch to just above a whisper and said, "Our plan is to create an interruption in the analog phone services. Having the cell phones cloned will cause the customers phone bills to skyrocket. This forces them to change over to the more impenetrable digital system." I thought to myself, "Yeah, right, does he really expect me to believe corporate America is going to resort to such illegal activities just to create a market to sell their products?" I was still having trouble understanding what Mr. Smith's angle was. He went on to say that he would handle the service interruption and poor service issues from his end. I would be in charge of the cloning, which would in turn create the enormous phone bills.

I was still skeptical. Was I being set up? Mr. Smith sensed my hesitancy. "Listen Kid, we are willing to supply you with 50,000 ESN numbers from all over the U.S. on a weekly basis, free and clear. What you do with those numbers is your own business, no questions asked," he says. "Here's the icing on the cake. I will even guarantee the ESN numbers will be good for sixty days and you and your organization will have no hassles from the FCC or any other law enforcement agency. In fact, if you have any problems with the competition out there, you just let me know and I will see that the police go in and shut them down." With a smirk he added, "Just like I had done with you fellows today."

Now it was all making perfect sense. That was no chance meeting between CC, Carlos, and the cops. This was a set up, only the other way around. Mr. Smith had me over a barrel and I was in no position to say no. My business had been shut down. Just when I thought I was all washed up in the cloning business, a better offer comes in.

There was silence for about twenty seconds. I pondered over the possibilities and the tremendous income potential.

Just to make sure I understood correctly, I ran the scenario back by him again. "You're going to just give me 50,000 ESN numbers a week. No strings attached. Right?" With a nod, Mr. Smith answered. "Right." "And I won't have any problems from the law or any competition from other cloners?" "That's about it," Mr. Smith replied. Had I missed something? This just seemed too good to be true. Mr. Smith then handed me a computer print out of 5,000 phone numbers along with the ESN numbers. He then said, "This is a little signing bonus to do with what you please. Well Greg, do we have a deal? If so, just give me a good phone number where I can reach you next week." Still slightly dazed, I gave him my pager number on the back of a book of matches. We shook hands, and parted ways.

That evening on my way home I kept checking my rear view mirror. I was still a bit suspicious about all the events that transpired earlier. Had I stumbled on that proverbial pot of gold at the end of the rainbow? Or were storm troopers about to bust down my door in the middle of the night and haul my ass off to jail. Well, if this was a set up, I was going to give them their money's worth. I couldn't sleep that night anyway, so I began working on a plan to distribute all those ESN numbers across the country. I made some calls to some players I knew back East in Washington D.C., Baltimore, and Chicago. I also had associates in several other metropolitan areas like Detroit, Kansas City, and even as far South as Atlanta.

I didn't want to say too much over the phone in case someone's line was tapped. I told them I had a real sweet deal for them, and if they were interested, to meet me in Las Vegas Saturday night. I would be staying at Caesar's Palace. Everyone knew the routine, as we usually met there twice a year anyway for a heavyweight fight or even just to gamble.

I took a night flight out of LAX on Friday. Just to make sure I was in Vegas to greet them as they began arriving on Saturday. That night we ordered room service in my suite including champagne and prime rib. After the food was ordered we started the meeting. There were about fifteen players that were able to make it on such short notice.

After everyone finished eating, I ran the game down. "I will supply each of you with at least 3,000 numbers each week along with the ESN numbers. Not only will I guarantee the numbers for sixty days, but also if you give me the names and addresses of competitors in your cities that are already cloning, I will see to it that they get shut down and are never able to operate again. On top of that, I can offer my word that no one in this room, or in your organization, will ever be criminally charged with cloning phones. You in turn will have to agree to purchase all the numbers in your area." There was a low murmur throughout the room. I continued, "This is how it will work. You will agree to buy all the numbers I send you for your area. Each number will cost you one hundred dollars. Payment is simple; Federal Express will show up at your door with a C.O.D. that has to be paid for by a cashier's check, or money order for the amount of numbers you will be receiving. In turn, I don't want any questions about where the numbers are coming from. Any questions?"

Pauly from Atlanta said, "Shit man, sounds pretty straight forward, but how many numbers will I get for my city? I mean, I can unload as many as you can give me at twice that price." I could see everyone was thinking the same thing. I told them, "You'll get anywhere from 500 to 3,000 numbers per week. If you can sell 3,000, then that will mean $300,000 dollars you'll owe. Now remember, you can sell those numbers for any price you want, say $200 dollars each, or even higher, because we will have taken care of your competitors and you will be the only game in town. Nobody loses. We all win. To start things rolling, I'm going to split up 5,000 numbers between you tonight at no charge. Now, who's in?" Everyone without exception nodded in agreement. We had to work out some minor logistics among some of the overlapping territories, but that didn't take too long. Now it was time to party. Tyrone, my Los Angeles representative, had driven up in a stretch limousine. We all piled into his limousine and headed down the strip for a night of gambling and chasing women. It was more like the babes chased us. We didn't get back to Caesar's until the sun came up.

It was the following Friday, when I received my first 12,500 numbers via a courier. I sorted them out according to the different areas we had set up in Vegas. I then sent them out via Federal Express. All of this was under different names and addresses. Everything went smoothly, and I grossed more than I could, or should I say some people, could spend in a lifetime. And that was just in the first week alone. It was almost too good to be true. Like clockwork those numbers kept coming in every Friday.

My associates were happy too. Kansas City was selling their numbers for $250 dollars a piece. It was like we'd found the goose that laid the golden egg. Money was coming in so fast it was hard to spend it all. I bought myself a new BMW convertible (of course it was equipped with a digital phone) and a three-bedroom condo on the beach. Life couldn't get much sweeter than this.

A few months later I was soaking in my Jacuzzi, just kickin' it, and doing some channel surfing. I came across one of those one-hour news programs. I think it was Dateline or maybe even 20/20. Low and behold, there was Mr. Smith being interviewed. I hadn't laid eyes on the infamous Mr. Smith since our original meeting in the bar several months before. There he was still dressed in that tacky sports coat telling the country that he had assembled a task force to fight the ever increasing and illegal high tech cloning of cell phones. I almost dropped the remote in the water. He had the nerve to look directly into the camera and say, "Let me warn you. If you're cloning phones, we will find you. And you will be prosecuted to the full extent of the law." What a load of shit! If only the American people knew what was really going on. The Fleecing of America!

It was good while it lasted, but like all good things, it came to an end. My cash cow didn't dry up for almost nine months. I made more money than I could have spent in twenty lifetimes. My associates also made a killing in those nine months. Some of them bought nightclubs, record companies, car dealerships, and one even purchased a fifteen million dollar Lear Jet. Unexpectedly, one Friday, Mr. Smith's courier dropped off 20,000 numbers with an enclosed note stating that this would be the final drop off. He graciously thanked me and said the project was successful and he no longer needed my services. He added that if something else came up in the future, he would keep me in mind.

Everyone made out except the phone customers. For every dollar I made, the phone companies made a thousand. They made their fortune by switching customers over to their digital lines. The manufacturers made their fortune by selling the new digital phones. Selling the phones brought in high revenue, which in turned drove up their stock and pleased their stockholders.

Now every time I see someone talking on a new digital cell phone, I have to laugh to myself, "If they only knew."

Bullet Proof

Times were good. I thought about the time that I was living the 'American dream'. I had a big home, big cars, big bank accounts, and a big ego. Times weren't just good for me, but also for my friends at Death Row Records. One of my good friends at the time was an executive at Death Row. We will call him Mark. My two sons called him Uncle Mark. When our schedules permitted, we would get together and take our boys to do the father and son thing. One particular weekend we decided to take our kids to Disneyland. Mark said he would drive so I could feel the seats of his brand new 600 Benz.

That morning Mark pulled up to my house about 9:00am playing some new tracks by Tupac. When I walked out of the house, I saw Mark with a big grin on his face. But his smile was not as big as mine when I saw those shiny 20-inch chrome rims. I opened the door for the kids to jump in the back with little Mark. They started screaming, "Daddy they have TV's in the seat." I jumped in the front and saw a third TV. in the dash. "This is tight," I told him. With a TV in each headrest and one in the dash we drove down the street. He told me about all the features in his car. "It has a 20 disc CD changer, a VCR, a play station hook up, a Global Positioning Navigation System, and bulletproof windows," Mark told us. I think the kids were more impressed by the bulletproof windows than I was. Knowing whom Mark worked for; he should have made sure the whole car was bulletproof. Before we jumped on the freeway we stopped for gas. While Mark went in to pay for the gas my eldest son asked, "Daddy, did someone try to shoot Uncle Marks windows out?" I replied, "of course not son." Then my little genius said, "Well, how do you know it's bulletproof like superman?" "Because the man who sold him the car told him it was and he paid extra for it," I tried to explain. There was a short pause of about 10 seconds when he replied, "I hope your right."

I always think about that occasion when I take on a new client who thinks their network is 100% hack proof. Companies spend hundreds of thousands of dollars, sometimes millions of dollars, to make sure no intruders penetrate their computer network.

I was trying to land a 'legal' job breaking into a company computer system so they could find the flaws in their million dollar electronic junk pile. I talked to the CEO of the company who claimed that his system was 100% hack proof and virus free. "O.k." I said, "Give me 60 days to penetrate your computers. If I don't get in, you pay me nothing. If I do get in, you pay me $1 million dollars, in cash." He gave me a look that said, "Is this guy crazy?" Before he could say another word, I said, "O.k., half a million." My fee for hacking into a network was $25,000 to $50,000 dollars. I just wanted to test him since he was so arrogant about his network. He responded by saying, "You're kidding, right?" Five minutes ago he was convinced that God himself could not penetrate his network. Now, by the look on his face, he wasn't so sure. So I thought I would break it down for him. "Let's look at this as a boxing match. In this corner, we have the champion, with a $5 million dollar IBM Network that is running operating systems by Microsoft, Sun Microsystems, and AT&T Unix. He also has security software made by Cylink Corporation and Watch Guard Technologies. 107 people holding bachelor degrees, 29 master degrees, and 10 PhD's manages his system. Four of them are from MIT. In the other corner, we have the challenger. He's from the Ghetto. Weighing in with a $3,000 dollar laptop computer, homemade software, and no college degrees. Now lets get ready to rumble." The big time CEO looked across his desk and gave me a small smirk. I think this is good. I told him, "One way of testing your network's susceptibility to the 'hacker threat', is to perform a penetration analysis. A penetration analysis is a powerful security assessment tool that will not only tell you specific vulnerabilities to which your networks and systems are exposed to, but if done correctly, will also highlight policy, proce-dural, and organizational weaknesses within your security architecture." That was something I picked out from a magazine or something. He started nodding his head so I knew I got to him. I decided to close the deal on a softer note by saying, "A penetration study is not so much about breaking in as it is about raising security awareness. A very intelligent person once said, 'so how do you know the windows are bullet proof unless they've been shot at?" He lied and said, "Yes I heard that before." I knew then I had him. He then blurted out, "$150,000 dollars and no more." Well, I thought, $50,000 dollars was going to be my fee, but I wanted him to feel that he had taken advantage of me, so I agreed. He spends millions of dollars on employees, hard-ware, and software, but he is too cheap to see if it all works. Plus for a CEO he is not too bright. He heard me tell him what type of computers, software, operating systems, and even the number of employees he has running his network. I thought this was easy. I pulled out a Confidentiality Pene-tration Agreement for him to sign. So once I break in, he has to pay me and not run to the Feds and say some unau-thorized hacker broke into their Fort Knox Network. With contracts signed and permission to attack, I left saying, "Lets get busy."

A true hacker does his homework about his target before he or she even sits down in front of the computer. This particular company was in the soft drink and fast food industry. They have well over 60,000 employees with offices on every continent. The bigger the company it is, the easier it is to hack. It's easy for a small company to keep track of their employees and the computers they work on. They can make sure that passwords are changed often and passwords are not their social security numbers, license plate numbers, birthdays, favorite colors, or their spouses or kids names.

I found there are three ways to penetrate a network. One way is to find a back door password. For instance, when you purchase some hardware or software it may come with a default password. Some people never change the default password. Secondly, one common misconception is that people think hackers are psychic. They see a hacker sitting in front of a computer predicting what a person would use as their password. A password may not be a word. It can be a letter or numbers or combination of both. Let's not forget you can have characters like -/.*#?&. Let's say the password had 'Dog' as part of it. If you throw in 1 & 2, -, or a *, the actual password could be 2dog-1 or D-o*g12. So if a hacker figures out your passwords, its not because he or she is psychic, but maybe you made it easy for him or her to figure it out. By writing your password on a piece of paper and throwing it away, hackers will dumpster dive trashcans outside of offices looking for passwords scribbled on yellow post-its. The third way, believe it or not, is the password that was just blatantly given to them. You may have thought you were giving it to someone else, but in reality it was a hacker. That's how I decided to get access to their network. Its what us hackers call 'Social Engineering'. What is 'Social Engineering'? It is an attempt by a computer hacker to persuade a legitimate system user to reveal confidential information, allowing the hacker (me) to break through security barriers. There are many types of social engineering attacks, but the most common of social engineering will come through the telephone. I'm going to persuade one of the employees to disclose his or her log on name and password to me.

First, I decided to do some 'Phreaking'. Phreaking is a hacker term that means: figuring out ways around the telephone company's equipment so you can make free calls, trace calls, or eavesdrop on conversations. My purpose for phreaking this day was to eavesdrop. You know that big 5x10x3 box that's a couple of feet away from the curb downtown, in your neighborhood, or across the street from your kid's school? It's usually pale green, although I have found some to be beige. It will usually have your phone companies name on it. A lot of these boxes can be open with a 7/16" Allen wrench. At least that is what it took to open the one 100 yards from my targets complex. Once you have the damn thing open, you can see all the phone lines in the area lined up, many of which are just unused lines. I didn't waste time stripping wires. I just hooked up the alligator chips of the handset directly to the screws. Once everything was hooked up I was able to listen to individual conversations of the 12,000 employees at this location. I then pulled out a FM transmitter and hooked up the alligator clips to a line in the box. Then I closed the box and locked it back up. I jumped into the rented Astro van and drove a quarter of a mile down the street. The radio was tuned to the station that was receiving the frequency of the transmitter.

I listened and recorded at least 12 hours of conversations, just waiting patiently to find my poor naïve accomplice. Then I found him. His name was Richard Watson. I heard him place a call to his wife telling her he was going to be late for dinner again. It was 4:05pm on Thursday. His wife sounded very disappointed. According to her, this was the third time this week he was late. She told him that this better not happen tomorrow because she had plans for a romantic night. He promised her he would not be late on Friday, but did tell her he may have to work that weekend, because his project was due on Monday. That's all I needed to know. A busy employee may not pay much attention to a call from the CD (computer department). Tomorrow about 4:00 p.m., one hour before he takes off for his romantic night and in a big hurry, I will make my move.

Social Engineering is another word for acting. It was five minutes to four on Friday when I started rehearsing my script. Just like Wesley Snipes did before he turned into Nino Brown in New Jack City. From the back of the Astro van with my cell phone in one hand and an A&W Root beer in the other, I dialed the main number to the beverage company. I was greeted by a young, sweet, innocent voice that asked, "How may I direct your call?" I said to her, "May I speak to Richard Watson." Seconds later I heard a raspy but hyper voice that said, "Watson." I took a deep breath and said, "Is this Richard Watson," he said, "Yes." I then went on to say, "Hi, this is John in CD. We're getting boot error messages on the main server that indicates an error in the format of your boot disk key file. It'll only take a second to fix. I need you to type in a couple of quick commands on your system, or if you'll just give me your user name and password, I can fix the problem really fast." I had no idea what I was talking about, but it's ok because he too had no idea what I was talking about, but he definitely felt the urgency in my voice! "OK," he said, "tell me what to do." I then went in for the kill. I gave him a heavy sigh, giving him the impression I was under pressure. "OK," I said in a rush, "first I am going to need you to log off the network and reboot your workstation. Once you logon back on to the network, type this command in the lower left screen: left click, run, command, dot, com, telnet, logon, back slash, USR, back slash, BIN, front slash, format, space, dash, ell, space, ETCV, back slash, fix, pipe, space, return." These commands meant nothing to him or me. He tried following my advice the best he could. I gave him those directions several times. After the third time he was feeling completely lost and incompetent. He felt the urgency in my voice each time he made a mistake. He struggled to type commands without understanding what they did. The pressure was rising. I told him, "Others are waiting." I then threw in, "If I don't get this solved now I will have to work through the weekend. And my marriage can't afford it." He said, "I know what you mean." I told him, "If you'll give me your logon I.D. and password, I can have it fixed in five minutes. You can even change your password when I'm done." By now it's about 4:20 p.m. He has to finish the project and get home to his wife. I waited only 3 seconds before he decided to give in. I told him, "Thank you and have a good weekend."

I would wait until Saturday before I penetrated the network, like a virgin on prom night. And just like prom night, I was in the Hilton Hotel doing what I do best. I sat my jet-black laptop on the desk with both hands. I opened it up very gently. I whipped out my long six-foot black power cable. When I inserted the cable in the back, my friend came alive with several loud beeps and a continuous hum that indicated that it was o.k. for me to run my fingers all over its soft, gentle keyboard. I pulled out another long cord. This one was gray and about 12 feet long. One end was plugged into the phone jack, and the other end I inserted into the other lonely hole (the modem). I turned my friend around, cracked my knuckles and said, "Enough four play, let's fuck". I logged into the Internet and Telnet over to my target. I was asked to enter a login name and password. I entered Richard's I.D. and password. Then I was greeted: Good afternoon Richard Watson, your last log on was yesterday at 4:15 p.m. I'm in, and now...$150,000 dollars richer. I knew they were looking for some back door trick and wouldn't expect me to walk through the front door. I logged on to the root directory and uploaded a .5k text file called YABH.sys (Your ass has been hacked). I then logged off. Unlike prom night with that virgin, I was in and out in two minutes.

Monday morning I called up the not-so-bright CEO. I told him to get the cashiers check made out and I will be at his office about 2pm. He responded by saying, "You got in? That's Impossible!" I said to him, "Like I told you before, if I don't get in you don't pay. Now call the accounting department and have them get me my money." I then hung up the phone. It was exactly 1:55 p.m. when I walked into the lobby. I approached who I thought was the sweet sounding receptionist on the phone last week. The women looked around 45 years old and 300 pounds. Like the old saying "If she sounds good over the phone she's ugly in person." I told her who I was and that I was expected. She made a call and directed me to the sales training room. I thought that was strange until I walked into the room. There were 27 employees from the computer department starring at me. No one said a word. I noticed that some of them were sweating. I then noticed there wasn't one Black face in the crowd. If I had known that, I think I would have charged double. Thirty seconds after being in the room, the CEO and the head of the computer department came in. The director of the computer department looked just like a horse. I gave him the nickname 'Mr. Ed'. He was the one who had a PhD from MIT. Before I could say a word, Mr. Ed dropped down on a table before me an 11" inch thick print out of all log files for the last two weeks. He starts screaming, "You're a fraud and should be arrested." He went on for two minutes before Mr. CEO stopped him. He said, "Mr. Evans, since our phone conversation this morning, I personally along with the other gentlemen in this room (I then noticed there were no women, I should have charged triple), could not find any signs of an illegal log on. So if you got in, prove it." I then cracked a smile. I looked around the room watching everyone watch me, and I'm thinking to myself, "They think they got me." I broke the silence and said, "There are enough people in here with degrees and high IQ's and they can't even boil water. You have all this talent, you have computer science majors and mathematicians, and with all this talent they over looked one thing. You were expecting me to come in the back door, when I walked straight through the front door." Everyone looked at each other crazy-like. The CEO said, "What do you mean?" I said, "I didn't try to hack my way in so it would show up in your log. I did what us computer hackers called 'Social Engineering'." When I said that, everyone except the CEO and I grunted. They then knew how I pulled it off. The CEO said, "What the hell is Social Engineering?" I explained, "I called into this company and asked for an employee. I then told this employee that I worked in your computer department and then convinced him to give me his username and password over the phone.

Now, go over to your computer and log on to the root directory and open a file called 'YABH.sys'. And then you can give me my money." Everyone rushed over to the computer. Mr. Ed switched to the root directory and there it was. I told him to open the file. When he read, 'Your ass has been hacked', all their faces dropped. No one said a word. The CEO reached into his jacket and handed me a cashier's check for $150,000 dollars made out in cash. I opened my briefcase to put the check away and to give him my full detailed report on how I did it. As I closed my briefcase, the CEO said, "I think we have an opening coming up." I smiled and said, "No thanks. You couldn't afford me." I walked to the door and stopped. Then I turned around and looked at everyone watching me leave. I looked them in their faces and said, "Amateurs."

As I walked through the parking lot, I pulled out my cellular phone and called Richard on the phone. I told him, "Listen very carefully. A carrier will drop off a very large cashier's check to you in less than an hour. Take a long vacation with your wife. Maybe have some kids. Right after the check gets to you, you will be fired. Sorry, and good luck."

The Money Tree

Back in 1991, before America On Line, the only thing available to the public on the Internet was Bulletin Board Services (BBS). If you wanted to talk to people over your computer, there were hundreds of thousands of BBS's available. But you needed a modem to access them. Competition between the BBS's was stiff. They were constantly trying to out do each other. Some promoted their BBS with pretty screens, or multi line chats, but the public wanted more speed so they could download faster.

At that time, most everyone was running at 2400 baud, even though 9600 baud and 14.4 baud were available. The problem was, the faster the modem the more expensive they were. This was a little too pricey for the average consumer to afford. They were selling for as much as $700 dollars a piece. Still there was no denying the need for more speed.

One day I was hanging out at Venice Beach. I was playing a few games of basketball with a couple of my friends. I was sitting on a bench catching my breath after a particularly close game when one of the guys from the other team came over to congratulate me on a good game. Before long we were sitting there together discussing all sorts of things from basketball to computers. He had introduced himself as Frank. In the course of our conversation he told me that he and his girlfriend worked for one of the world's largest computer software and hardware distributors based out of Orange County. Frank said he had a cushy job in shipping and his girlfriend, whom he met at work, held a position in New Accounts. Like a bolt of lighting, all of a sudden it hit me. I didn't waste anytime asking Frank if he would like to go to Roscoe's Chicken and Waffles to discuss a business proposition.

During our dinner, I proposed to Frank that I would pay him and his girlfriend $1,000 dollars for every account they set up for me, and 10% of all the profits from any of the merchandise they were able to get for me. If Frank could get me a few cases of modems, I'd give him 10% of what I could unload them for. Frank said he'd have to talk it over with his girlfriend first, but he would be sure to get back to me with his answer. It wasn't even three hours later when Frank rang me back on my cell phone and said that the deal was on.

The following Monday, I applied for a business license under the name of Modem Depot (not really, but I wasn't going to tell you the real name). I then phoned Franks company and set up a new account with his girlfriend. The standard operating procedure was to set up their new accounts with net 30 days. This means I could receive my order and not have to pay for 30 days. I figured that I probably wouldn't have to pay anything anyway. After the initial 30-day period, the account would be turned over to the general accounting department. This was where Frank's girlfriend's friend Tricia worked. Tricia was also in need of money. She was willing to "accidentally" loose the account file.

I opened a mailbox at a local Mail Boxes Etc service store. It was a branch where a friend of mine worked. That way, I had a working address that was hard to trace and I could still receive shipments from my new account. Plus I had a good friend to warn me if someone was watching my box or a set-up was in the works. Our plan was to have him page me with the code 666 if there was a problem. Then I would know not to show up and pick up my packages. The first order I placed on my new account was for 100 modems, 60 U.S. Robotics dual standard HST's, 10 Boca 14.4's, 20 Supra 14.4's with programmable chips, and a few Hayes Ultra 14's.

Here was my plan: Since there was such a demand for modems, but the high cost made them unaffordable for the majority of users, I would start a Rent-to-Own type of company. The customer would put $200 dollars down and pay $25 dollars a week for their modems. And of course I would charge the usual $15 dollar late fee plus an additional $2.50 daily after the due date. I also tacked on a $40 dollar shipping and handling charge, which actually cost me about $15 dollars. After doing my numbers, I figured if I could rent out 100 modems in the first month, by the second month I could be bringing in a profit of $10,000 dollars. This is minus the advertising and the payoff to Frank, his girlfriend, and her friend Tricia.

My advertising costs were relatively low since I was getting the modems for free. I took out a full-page ad in one of those newspapers that sold everything from appliances to used cars and even farm animals. If you could name it, they sold it. The ad read in bold print: Own a U.S. Robotics, Hayes, Supra, or Baca 14.4K modem for only $25 dollars a week. The ad came out on Thursday and by the following Monday I had rented 100 modems and had orders for 50 more. This was taking off faster than even I had anticipated. I needed to hire help just to process the applications, take orders, and start up an accounting department of my own. By the second week, we had doubled our orders.

I had created a money tree, and in order to keep the tree producing money, I had to cultivate it. First of all, I had to ensure my business partners were happy, so I increased their new account set up bonus to $3,000 dollars and guaranteed them $500 dollars a week. This I promised even if the accounts were not being actively used. Secondly, I needed to work on expanding the business, so I began running newspaper ads nationwide. Before long, my business had quadrupled.

The money tree grew strong and was producing faster than I could harvest it all. I needed a new business to invest some of the money in. I decided to branch out into a chain of pager stores. I was buying up one to three operating pager stores a week by just approaching the owner with an on the spot cash offer. If the owners were not interested in my offer, I would just walk out. Somehow the store that turned me down would be mysteriously broken into and vandalized. I would again approach the owner with another cash offer, only this time I offered them considerably less. They were usually ready to sell by this time. This was the basis I used for future hostile takeovers.

While I was busy trying to get my new business venture off of the ground, the roof was about to collapse around my money tree. The problem started when Frank began sleeping around with Tricia, his girlfriend's friend whom worked in accounting. When his girlfriend found out, she up and quit on me. She didn't care about the money anymore, and besides, there were rumors' circulating around that the company was about to conduct an internal audit. Frank was concerned. He feared that his ex-girlfriend was so upset that she might roll over on us if she was implicated.

I had Frank meet me for dinner at a waterfront restaurant in Newport Beach that evening to try and figure out what we were going to do about this mess. Frank had gotten accustomed to the lifestyle the money he was making had brought him. He had just purchased a new red Mustang convertible with cash, and had a house in escrow that he did not want to lose. He couldn't imagine returning to the life of trying to make ends meet on his $12 dollar an hour shipping job.

No one loved the money more than I did. After all, I was making $100,000 dollars a month in profits from our arrangement. I had brought a mini tape recorder with me just in case I needed a little extra insurance down the road. I worked the subject of the conversation to what we were going to do about his ex-girlfriend. I began working him up by telling him stuff like, "Not only are we going to lose our money tree, but we will end up in jail for so long, our dicks would fall off before we ever got out." Finally he reached the logical conclusion I had lead him up to and he said, "She got to get got." I said innocently, "What do you mean she got to get got?" He responded angrily, "The bitch got to die or we are going to jail." I had gotten what I needed from

Frank and switched off the recorder. I told him I'd take care of her. First I'd send someone to talk to her, and if she still did not come around we would deal with that later.

On my way home from dinner, my thoughts turned to another frustration, which was one of a more personal nature. I was wondering whom I could get to meet me when I got home and take care of my current personal frustration.

I decided to give Melanie a call from my cell phone. Melanie was beautiful and had a body that wouldn't quit. The only problem was that she was a gold digger. She loved money almost as much as I did, and she was always up front about it. I guess that is why we got along together. She agreed to meet me. She was sitting in my driveway in the car that I loaned her the money for, when I pulled up. Getting out of her car, she said, "I'm glad you called. I have something I wanted to talk to you about." I knew what that something was - it was money. It was always about money with Melanie but I also knew she'd fuck the Hell out of me first before bringing up the subject. It worked for me, I got what I wanted and she usually ended up getting what she wanted - the money.

After about an hour of good sex, and just when I was ready to doze off, she began her whining about how she needed $1,500 dollars and how fucked up it was for me to sleep with her and not help her out with her financial problems. I'd heard this script from her before. Melanie was just getting wound up when the phone rang. On the other end was an employee of mine whom I had sent over to intimidate Frank's ex-girlfriend. He was calling to tell me that she had never shown up at her home. I didn't think much about it at the time. I told him to hang tight and wait another hour or so as it was already midnight. As I hung up the phone, Melanie picked up right where she left off. In an attempt to drown her out I clicked on the television. There was breaking news about another Southern California case of road rage. The broadcaster recapped the details of the killing of a young woman who worked at an Orange County company. She was shot three times in the head, on the 55 freeway. When I realized that they were talking about Frank's ex-girlfriend, I quickly picked up the phone and called my guy that was in his car waiting for her in front of her place. I let him know he should call it a night and I wouldn't need him any more tonight.

I had mixed emotions at that point about Frank's ex. On one hand, I was distraught about her violent death at the hands of gang bangers just looking for a target to release their rage, yet her untimely death worked out perfectly for me. She could no longer rollover on my operation or me. I lost a friend and my business just went down the drain. That money tree had produced for over six months. I had made enough money to plant another money tree - my pager chain stores. That's what I'll do with the $900,000 dollars I'd made.

The Memory Game

About one year later I was at one of those mega computer stores that specialized in computers and all of the paraphernalia that was associated with them. I inquired of one of the clerks what the cost of an 8 Meg Simm chip would run. The clerk told me that a memory chip like that would cost in the range of $250 dollars. I was appalled, how could they charge that much? I realized right then and there that I could market these chips if I could get them cheap enough and make a sizable profit. My thoughts immediately flashed back to my old partner Frank.

That afternoon when I got back to my office, I contacted my so-called "agent" or "broker" Nick. Nick always knew a buyer or someone else to unload merchandise and he knew the going street price on merchandise. I asked Nick about the memory chips and he told me he'd check around and get back to me. As promised, Nick called back the next day and told me he could get me $150 dollars per memory chip, and that he had a buyer already who would take all I could get for that price.

My next step was to contact Frank to see if he wanted in. I hadn't spoken with Frank in almost a year and I wasn't quite certain how he'd react to hearing from me after all that went down a year ago. I called the number I had for him and got a pre recorded message stating his number had been changed to an unpublished listing. That was no problem for me. I would just call one of my girls, named Carmen, who worked at Pacific Bell to get me his new number.

Carmen was a sweet caramel complected girl who also happened to be a nymphomaniac. She used to come to my office in nothing but a long Georgio Jacket and a pair of high heels. She did things to me you'll only see in XXX videos. I remember once she came in and closed the doors to my private office while I was on a conference call with my attorney and the U.S. Attorney. She gave me one of the best blowjobs I ever had. Thank God video conferencing wasn't available back then. Carmen would get me unlisted phone numbers, copies of peoples phone bills, match phone numbers to specific addresses, and I in turn would make her car payments. Carmen informed me that Frank had his number changed about one week after the tragic death of his girlfriend a year ago, and then gave me his new unlisted number.

That evening I gave Frank a call at his home. As I had expected, he wasn't pleased to be hearing from me again. I told him I needed to meet with him. I could tell by the hesitance in his voice he wasn't excited about the idea.

I informed him I could show up sometime when it would be less opportune for him, or he could just meet me at Baker's Drive-In after work tomorrow for a cup of coffee. Reluctantly he agreed to meet me in the parking lot about 7 p.m. the next day.

I made arrangements with a couple of my associates to run surveillance at Bakers before 7 p.m. I sent another man to follow Frank from work to ensure there was no one tailing him.

It was about 7:05 p.m. when I spotted Frank's candy apple red Mustang pulling into the Baker's parking lot. I caught Frank's roving eyes as he got out of his car and I waived him over to my new Infinity Q45. We drove through the drive through and picked up a couple of coffees under the watchful eyes of my men, who were following.

At the first red light we came to I leaned across the seat and patted Frank down the chest, stomach, and around the collar to make sure he wasn't wearing a wire or anything else. Frank said, "What the fuck are you doing man?" It was a rhetorical question that I needed not answer. By this time I knew I had his complete attention, and I tossed him a cassette tape labeled "Frank". I told him to go ahead and put it in the tape deck. I could tell by the confused look on his face he did not have a clue to what this was all about. As the tape played, Frank's eyes about popped out of his head when he realized that I had taped the part of our conversation over dinner the night his girlfriend was shot on the freeway a year ago. There it was, on tape for the whole world to hear Frank saying, "The bitch has got to die."

Frank ripped the tape out of the tape deck and flashed me a look. If looks could kill, this was one of them. A second later he said, "Okay, what is it that you want from me?" I answered, "Memory, lots and lots of memory chips." Frank responded, "The company doesn't do business like they used to, now they check bags and purses when we leave work. How do you expect me to get them out?" I told Frank to duct tape the chips to various parts of his body and just walk them out. He thought briefly and then said he could get me 1,000 8 Meg chips a week and asked if that would be enough. I did the math, and told him I only wanted 4,000 and he had 6 weeks to deliver. I knew he wouldn't be able to carry this off any longer than 6 weeks without getting caught. With that I told him that I would give him the cassette tape and $25,000 dollars for his time. Frank seemed genuinely pleased with the deal. We agreed to meet again on Friday at the same place and same time. I then dropped him off back at his car.

I immediately called my agent from my cell phone to finalize the deal and give him the details of the delivery arrangements of the memory chips. I told Nick I would need half in cash and the rest sent to my accounts upon delivery.

I was driving down the 91 East freeway, listening to my theme song, "For the love of money," from the New Jack City soundtrack, when I received a page from a 303 area code. I called the page number. It was Tracy, a flight attendant from New York calling from Denver to let me know she was on her way to Los Angeles. She had eighteen hours to kill before her turn-around flight back. Tracy and I often met at the airport Hilton for a night of sex. I wouldn't call it love making because we were not in love, just lust. I told her I'd go ahead and get a suite and I would meet her there at 9:00 p.m.

By 9:15 Tracy was on all fours, and I was behind her sweating like a run away slave. The Isley Brothers set the tempo in the background as Tracy moaned out loud "More, harder, more." I was thinking to myself "God I'm good", when all of a sudden it hit me like a ton of bricks. Something wasn't right with this deal with Frank. There was no way in Hell he could get 1,000 chips a week. At most, I figure he might be able to get 500 a week out. Besides, he didn't even question me about the tape or why I had recorded it. He didn't even ask what I planned to do with it or if there were other copies. Nor did he haggle over the terms or ask for an advance. That was not like Frank.

I pulled away from Tracy in mid stroke and reached over for the phone. Tracy collapsed on the bed next to me in total exhaustion, and let out a sigh of satisfaction. I called my agent Nick to let him in on my suspicions. He too thought something seemed a little bit fishy and suggested we contact a private investigation firm. We often did business out of San Diego with this firm to bug homes and put tails on people. Nick said he'd contact the firm for me first thing in the morning.

By the time I got off of the phone with Nick, Tracy was out on the balcony stark naked watching the planes land and take off. Tracy beckoned me over and I obliged. We stood out on the balcony in silence as a hot dry breeze caressed our naked bodies.

Tracy and I slept in late the next morning. While Tracy was in the bathroom dressing in her uniform, I checked my voicemail. There was a message, stating the private investigation firm was on it. The cost was $20,000 dollars for bugging, tailing, and to do a background and credit check. I thought the price was a little steep but hell if Frank were clean, I'd be making $150,000 dollars a week off of the deal. If not, than $20,000 dollars was a fair price to stay out of jail.

Two days before our arraigned meeting, Frank called and said he had 3,000 chips ready to be delivered tomor-

74
www.hitechhustler.com

row. I put him off by saying, "I'm on the other line. I'll call you back later," and then I hung up. I hadn't received a report yet from San Diego so I gave them a call. The investigator on the case informed me that he had observed three Orange County Sheriff's cars at Franks warehouse on several occasions and Frank was staying at what used to be an Embassy Suite Hotel in Tustin. His credit report showed that all his bills were current. It was the investigators opinion that this was probably a police set up. That's just as I had suspected.

I then phoned a friend in Virginia and asked him to call Frank from a payphone to his cell phone number and tell him I wasn't free to talk right now and that he should stick with our original plans for delivery.

At that point I decided to get out of town and put some distance between Orange County and myself. That evening I caught a red eye to Las Vegas to go and see Tamara, a beautiful girl who used to work for Crazy Horse II. It was the best strip club in town. The following day I was down at the tables inside Caesars hotel, shooting dice at $1,000 dollars a roll while the arraigned meeting was supposed to be taking place back in California.

I decided to go home that Saturday on a Southwest Airlines flight. As I stepped off of the plane at Ontario airport several FBI agents greeted me. That wasn't all. Airport Security, and a handful of Orange County Deputy Sheriffs also greeted me. They were not putting me under arrest, but just wanted to ask me some questions about a car bombing that took Frank's life, and destroyed 3,000 memory chips with it.

Once at the station I placed my one phone call to Shawn Chapman. Shawn worked for Johnny Cochran's office and she was what I called every black man's dream. She had a hard athletic body, beautiful hair that hung past her shoulders, and her voice was as sexy as her thighs. She was my knight in shinning armor. Ms. Chapman was at the Police station within two hours. Thirty minutes later I was walking out the station door. No charges were ever filed against me. Not that there should have been. I hadn't done anything wrong this time.

I never did find out what went down with Frank and the car bombing. The only thing I can come up with is that maybe I wasn't the only one Frank was rolling over on to the cops. All I can tell you is that I might be a lot of things to a lot of people, but a killer I am not.

I can't say that I wasn't planning on how to get back at Frank for setting me up, but my plan was to send the cassette anonymously to the detective investigating his girl-friend's shooting. I figured he'd be trying to explain himself to the cops for quite a while. I never even considered anything violent, but I guess someone else wasn't quite as forgiving. Thanks for the money Frank.

Pirates of the Caribbean

It was a crisp fall Sunday, the Northeastern foliage had already peaked and the trees were almost bare. I knew I should be out raking but the New York Jets were playing at the Meadowlands. I was comfortably seated in my Lazy Boy in front of a big screen TV. I figured the raking could be put off for a couple of more hours.

Half way through the third quarter my pager went off. I recognized the number to be from Darrell, a one time crimey of mine in New Jersey. I glanced at the score in the corner box of the TV. The Jets were down by 13. Had the score been closer, Darrell would of just had to wait till the end of the game. I picked up my cell phone from the table next to my recliner and dialed Darrell's number from the read out on my pager.

Darrell picked up after the first ring and sounded rather breathless as he began to relay the urgency of his situation. With the same breathlessness, he explained to me that he had acquired over 1,000 new laptop computers. A couple of guys had heisted them from a warehouse, and because there was a lot of heat, he couldn't get them out of the city to unload them. He then went on to say that the local and state police were everywhere and they even had the helicopters searching the freeways. It didn't sound like the kind of high profile crime that would cause the State Police to set up roadblocks or anything. Then he told me that a security officer at the warehouse wandered in at the wrong time and had been critically injured during the heist. Reports of the robbery were on every channel in the Tri-State Area. I now understood the urgency and the fear in Darrell's voice. This wasn't just grand theft. And he didn't want to get caught with the laptops. I normally don't get involved in situations like this and I normally would have told him not to call back, but Darrell and I went way back. He had put his ass on the line for me several times in the past. I felt I owed him one.

Darrell was obviously scared and wanted to unload the laptops for whatever he could get at this point. He just wanted to disassociate himself from possible murder charges if the Security Officer didn't make it. I told Darrell to sit tight and keep his cool. I would handle everything and get back to him in an hour.

Into the fourth quarter the Jets were now only trailing by six when I began to put my plan into effect. I knew a fence down in the Bahamas that could move just about everything from bonds, art, cars, currency, or electronics. I had dealt with him before and knew he wouldn't have any problems getting up a large sum of money on short notice.

He had always been discrete in the past. The laptops I had recently seen at one of those large computer chain stores were selling for $3400 dollars each. If I could get my fence to agree to $2,000 dollars each, I could give Darrell $1000 dollars, and keep $1,000 dollars for myself. This was a lot of money from a fence, plus laptops were a hot item then and brought top dollar. As best as I could figure, that was a cool million for me, and if I worked everything out right, I could have this whole deal wrapped up and be back home in time for Monday Night Football.

I grabbed my jacket and headed a couple of miles down the road to a nearby Laundromat. There were just two shabbily dressed women in the back at the folding tables, when I began feeding five-dollar bills into the change machine. The woman in the back stopped their folding just long enough to listen to the silver hitting the metal tray. You'd think I had just hit the jackpot in Atlantic City by the looks on their faces. I gathered up the quarters and moved several feet down to the payphone and began dialing Terrance Jr., or TJ, in the Bahamas. Through the use of heavy slang and a semi-coded language, I told TJ what I had in the way of laptops. I told him how many I had and let him know what it would cost him. I let him know that I would be there with the merchandise within 24 hours. TJ said he'd have "no problem mon" getting the money together by then. I told him I'd call in about an hour on his personal line before my arrival and we'd set up a meeting place, then I hung up.

The clock was ticking and I had to hurry if I was to make it back by Monday night. I used up the rest of my quarters to call Darrell back. He sounded less panicked since the last time I spoke with him. I told him he had about one and a half hours to rent a small U-Haul and meet me at a little known rural airport about twenty miles out of town. I'd meet him there by Hanger #5. My next call was to an airline charter company that I knew could and would be ready on a moments notice. It was a small time operation. The owners took turns being pilot and mechanic. They always appreciated my business. The guys knew I always paid cash and gave a hefty bonus if they were ready for take off on the drop of a dime.

I drove back home to grab some cash and to pack clothes for a warmer climate. I don't know why, but while I was grabbing some stacks of cash out of my safe, I picked up my 9mm Ruger and a small .25 caliber automatic for back up. I tossed them in the bag as well and then headed out to the airstrip.

Upon reaching the airport I spotted Darrell and the U-Haul at the meeting place. It was dusk by then. I surveyed the surrounding area for anything suspicious before approaching the hanger. Darrell got out the driver's side and followed me into the hanger. The pilot was making last minute checks on the outside of the Lear Jet when I caught his eye. After the usual handshakes and greetings I pulled out half of the cash amount we had agreed upon. Plus an additional thousand if we could take off as soon as the plane was loaded. His smile widened as he nodded.

Once we were underway and a safe distance from the tower, I pulled out my black book and used the phone on the jet to call Bob at his yacht charter company on the Southeast coast of Florida. I knew there was no way the jet could get through Customs if we landed in the Bahamas. So I made prior arrangements to charter a yacht. I liked doing business with Bob. I had done business with him before. He wasn't the cheapest, but his employees were discrete and he always had a large selection of motor yachts fueled up and ready to go. For an extra grand he could pretty much guarantee that his boats and customers wouldn't have any hassles from the Coast Guard. I'm not sure if it was a pay off or they just had some sort of good working relationship. But, it was well worth it for me to pay the added insurance.

Bob remembered me from our last dealings. I told him I needed at least an 85-foot yacht with a crew. I also told Bob that I wanted to leave a couple of hours before daybreak in order to get some early morning fishing in. He assured me he'd have the boat stocked and ready by 3:00 am. He also offered to send a car to the airport to pick up our group. Because we had so much gear and diving equipment with us, I suggested he send a couple of commercial vans instead. Bob knew I was neither a sports fisherman nor a diver, but figured he wasn't being paid an inflated rental price to ask questions about my cargo. In fact I'm sure he'd rather not know.

After hanging up with Bob, I reclined my seat and closed my eyes feeling very pleased with myself. Everything was working like a well-oiled machine. The yacht would be loaded under the cloak of darkness and by daybreak, we'd be well on our way to the Bahamas to pick up our money. After a short nap I woke to the sound of the landing gear descending. I could see the lights of South Florida out the cabin window, sparkling like a diamond necklace against the coastline.

As the plane taxied to the hanger I spotted Bob's large van and a guy in a flowered shirt, khakis, and dock shoes leaning against the dab. I assumed he also doubled as a crewmember besides his current position as a driver. As I exited the plane the warm humid Florida air slapped me in the face. It was a far cry from the nippy crisp climate we just left hours ago In New Jersey.

The van driver approached the plane and introduced himself as our first mate Dave. I instructed Darrell and his two flunkies to start unloading the plane. After we placed our personal luggage in the van I joined in on the make shift bucket brigade, along with Darrell, Dave, and the pilot. Among the six of us we had the vans loaded in about twenty minutes. We then headed towards the marina, which was just a few short miles away.

As promised, Bob had our yacht ready and waiting. Bob was there to welcome us aboard and introduce us to our crew. There was Captain Bob Green who from his age, looked like a seasoned sailor. Our cook for the voyage was Ramon. Our steward was Ray. He attended to our needs. Last but not least there was Dave, who met us at the airport.

As Ray showed us the amenities of the yacht and our quarters, Darrell supervised the loading of the laptops into the master stateroom. I figured the trip wouldn't take more than eight hours. We would probably be kicking it in the main salon for most of the trip and would not need our staterooms.

It was almost 3:00 a.m. as we headed out of the harbor past the breakwater into open sea. Ray our steward, served up light snacks of pate', cheese, crackers, and drinks. The swells were fairly heavy from the tropical storm that had recently passed through the area. The boat pitched from side to side. I could see a paleness come over the faces of Darrell and his crimies. Before long, people were heading to the topside deck to get some fresh air and to hang over the railings. Somehow, through intense concentration I managed to keep everything down, unlike my traveling companions up on the deck.

The sun was just starting to come up on the horizon when Darrell hurried into the main salon and announced that there were two boats approaching. I jumped up from the couch and made my way to the closet porthole. Sure enough, on our starboard side were two boats running parallel to each other, approaching rapidly. I first thought it was the Coast Guard, but as they got closer I could tell they didn't have the usual Coast Guard markings. Plus we seemed to be too close to the islands for the U.S. Coast Guard to be pulling us over. Just then, Captain Green turned hard to Port, and gave it full throttle. We all about lost the little food in our stomachs at the sharp turn and fast acceleration.

Dave came running into the salon, "I'm not sure what the fuck these guys want, but whatever it is we're not going to make it easy for them to get it." As we went from side to side, trying to get a better perspective from the different portholes, it was becoming obvious we weren't gaining any distance. In fact they were gaining on us.

As the boats came upon us, they split up, one going on each side of our bow. Dave grabbed a handgun from a locked cabinet and tossed a flare gun to Ray. They took off for the pilothouse while yelling back to us to stay down. I took this as my clue to retrieve my guns from my briefcase. I had never shot at anything living before and I wasn't quite sure if I was up to the task. Who knows, it just might work as a bluff, if push came to shove. I handed the .25 caliber to Darrell and kept the big gun for myself. After all I wanted all the advantage I could get. It was already loaded with a full clip, so all I had to do was release the safety, aim, and fire. I signaled to Darrell "let's go," and we started up the narrow staircase towards the outside deck. Just as I reached the final step, I heard gunfire. I froze where I stood. I could tell the gunfire was being returned from the pilothouse. After what seemed like forever, and numerous shots being exchanged, Captain Green let off of the throttle and killed the engines. The gunfire ceased and I could finally poke my head up out of the stairwell and look out to see what was going on. As I opened the door to the deck the sight of a gun barrel in my face got my immediate attention. I was nose to nose with a Hispanic man gesturing me with his AK-47 to give up my gun. I wasn't about to argue with him. I handed over my gun. Darrell managed to hide the small .25 auto. out of sight. The guy took my weapon and threw it over the railing into the water. He then motioned with his rifle for us to move back down below. Darrell and I turned tail, retreating back down the stairs. The Hispanic male whom had now been joined by two others followed us at gunpoint. They were recklessly waiving their guns around, and shouting commands in Spanish. One of the pirates held us in the salon at gunpoint while the other two began to search the rest of the staterooms. Just as they discovered the laptops, four other Hispanic men escorted Captain Green, Dave and Ray into the salon at gunpoint. Ray was holding on to his left arm. It appeared he'd taken a bullet. From the small amount of blood on his shirt I could tell it was just a nick.

We were all motioned to get down on the floor, face down, and two of the men began systematically binding our hands and feet with duck tape. There we were, the seven of us laying face down bound up like a rump roast. I was hoping the laptops would be enough of a diversion for the pirates that they wouldn't want to be bothered with killing us. The pirates continued to ransack the boat for guns, jewelry and just about everything they could turn around and sell for a quick buck. One guy even emptied out the silverware drawer after relieving us of our chains, rings, and watches. While a couple of pirates did the ransacking, the rest of them began to load the laptops up on deck and into their boats. I was waiting for them to carry up the last load and send someone back down to finish us off when I heard the engines of both boats start and pull away. I didn't realize that I'd been holding my breath, but when the sounds of their engines faded, I let out an audible sigh. I lifted my head and then rolled to my side in an attempt to sit up. I finally inched my way up a wall and got into an upright position. Once up, I noticed Ramon wasn't on the floor with everyone else. I asked, "Hey, what happened to Ramon?" The Captain lifted his head and said, "I didn't see him on deck, and I hope he's not laying dead somewhere. Has anyone seen him since the gunfire?" Dave mumbled "no" and several other people shook their heads no. Just then Ramon came down the hallway into the salon, rambling on in half English and half Spanish. He said something about "pince bendejos". Ramon got a knife from the gallery and as he began cutting everyone loose he muttered something about hiding in "el bano". I don't speak Spanish but I know that means bathroom. It seemed he had the best idea of any of us at the time.

After our release, Captain Green put his hand on my shoulder and asked, "Well son, what course do you want to take now? It's your boat, you've paid for it." I gave our situation considerable thought, "Might as well keep our course to the Islands. We're almost there anyway." That way it would give me a little more time to re-evaluate the situation and try to come up with something. Plus I had the ever-increasing idea that we'd been set up and paybacks were a possibility.

When we got to port a short time later, I called TJ on his private number. I didn't let on to TJ that anything was different than we'd discussed earlier. With slight hesitation and stumbling in his voice, TJ admitted he'd just received a call from another so called associate with the same product that I had offered him. The guy he was talking about only wanted about one half the price we'd agreed on. Not only had we been set up, but also these idiots didn't even know what the stuff was worth. We decided to meet at a beachfront restaurant and see if we could come to some arrangement. I didn't know for sure if TJ was involved in the Hijacking or not. After all, there was the possibility that TJ was just trying to make both deals. I did not think that TJ knew we'd been jacked, unless he was involved in it.

Darrell, his two crimies, and myself sat at this thatched roof open restaurant, drinking tropical drinks, and watching bikini clad ladies on the beach. It was a nice way to chill while we waited for TJ. Darrell was accumulating quite a few small umbrellas from his drinks and was lining them up around the table. Darrell and I rehashed the morning's events and came to the conclusion that TJ had probably set us up or was in collusion with the hijackers. By the time TJ arrived Darrell had worked himself up into frenzy, believing TJ was the culprit behind all the occurrences that befell us earlier in the day.

No sooner did T.J. take a seat than Darrell stuck my .25 auto. under the table and into TJ's crotch. I forgot that Darrell even had my gun until now. Before I could get a word out, Darrell glared into TJ's eyes as if he was the Devil himself, and muttered in a low, deep, slow, voice, "If you mother fuckers don't get my shit back from those mother fuckin' Spics now, I'm going to put a bullet through your motha-fucking balls. Just before I put one into your brain, along with anyone else's if they get in my way, you know what I mean?" The look of terror in T.J.'s face let on that he knew Darrell was dead serious about his threat. When TJ finally broke the stare and spoke, he was stuttering, "Ey Mon, I'll get your shit for you, no problem, and then we can still do our deal, right?" For a minute I thought that Darrell just wanted to kill TJ anyway, but when I put my hand on his shoulder, he leaned back in his chair and gave TJ a very reluctant nod. TJ excused himself to the next table, knowing that Darrell was not going to let him out of his sight.

He said that he had a few calls to make and he'd have our shit back to us within the hour.

It was one of those perfect days in paradise and I really didn't mind hanging out in the comfort of the shade. I liked drinking fresh tropical drinks and critiquing the babes strutting along the beach. Darrell said as his homies nodded in agreement, "Hey you see that bitch over there in the yellow thong? I'd like to get a piece of that." I reminded them what we were here for. Darrell took my comment as a challenge. Darrell must have been feeling a little better about his laptops, because he handed me the gun and said to keep an eye on TJ. Then he sprinted down the beach after the dark skinned girl in the yellow thong. He was fully dressed in his baggy's and high top Nikes I add. It was a lost cause from the get go. She wouldn't even give him the time of day. Darrell slinked back to our table spouting how she wasn't worth his time anyway. Darrell grabbed back my gun and continued to stare at TJ sitting at the next table.

It hadn't been more than 30 minutes when TJ returned. This time two white guys accompanied him. They were decked out like a couple of tourists, except they lacked the usual tan or the recently acquired red flow of sunburn. Instead their skin was milk white. You could tell before they even spoke that they were a couple of Englishmen. TJ skipped the usual formalities of introductions and just told us, "These guys are friends of mine and they know where and how to retrieve your shit. For a price." I still wasn't convinced TJ hadn't set us up for the hijacking, but we were over a barrel. Besides, if we didn't settle this soon, Darrell was going to kill TJ. His failure with the girl in the yellow thong did not help his mood improve any. TJ's acquaintances, the Englishmen, said that they'd get our stuff back from the 'damn Cubans' that stole it for $250,000 dollars. They said that this amount would just cover their expenses. It came down to either making a deal with the Englishmen or going home empty handed with nothing to show except a pile of bills and TJ's balls. I knew damn well the Limeys were the ones behind the Hijacking.

Darrell had his right hand down the waistband of his pants as he reminded T.J. of his prior threat. T.J. swallowed hard and with a most convincing tone, persuaded the Englishmen that it would be beneficial for all to cop a deal with us for $50,000 dollars, if they ever wanted to do business in the Islands again. Reluctantly the Englishmen agreed, but only after T.J. kicked in another fifty thousand that he would end up taking off the gross of what he was paying us. I never found out what the real connection between T.J. and the Englishmen was. It all worked out in the end. The way I figured it, the Englishmen had some

Cubans that worked for them as pirates. They would sail up and down the coast of the Islands and probably from Florida to Jamaica to Bahamas hi-jacking drug runners or even families on a weekend trip. Either way it goes we got paid. The Englishmen got paid, TJ got his computers, and Darrell let him keep his balls in the deal. Back in the states the security guard that got shot was fine. The heist of the computers was on the local news for about week. The cops claimed they had a lot of leads but they had nothing. One of the cronies that Darrell had hired to help move the computers down to the islands got busted a year later on unrelated but more serious charges. He tried to cut a deal with the police about the guard who got shot. The cops were very interested in what he had to say. I learned that an hour into his story the cops didn't believe the part about pirates hi-jacking the evidence. He is in jail today doing 20 to 25 years.

A fox In The Hen House

New York is commonly known as the city that never sleeps. In New York you can always find a fine eatery willing to serve dinner at one o'clock in the morning or a club that doesn't even open their doors until midnight. Despite catering to insomniacs, New York City comes across as closed and isolated, just the opposite of Los Angeles. Even though most of Los Angeles rolls up their streets when the bars close around 2:00 am, its people are much more approachable than New Yorkers. It is not uncommon to see movie stars, or celebrities, roller-skating or playing Frisbee with their dogs on the beach. It's not uncommon having lunch at an outdoor cafe on the street during a warm summer day. Los Angeles, because of it's laid back attitude, makes its celebrities more accessible. Also, because of this attitude, I was able to attend Shaquille O'Neal's birthday party. I had never met Shaq in person, but I was a big fan and an admirer of his. I could always be found courtside when the Lakers played home games. It was my friend, Deshawn, who worked at a studio in Hollywood, where Shaq was recording, who actually gave me the invitation to the party at the popular Olympic Connection in Beverly Hills.

Deshawn and I arrived at the club in my limousine. The parking lot looked like a damn exotic car show. There were custom and luxury cars of every shape and size from Hummers to Ferrari Testarosas. There were Rolls Royce's, Lotus's, and about one hundred limousines with their drivers waiting around for their cue to pick up their clients at the door.

Deshawn and I had my driver let us out right next to a sign that stated, "Closed to the public - Private party." After giving our name to the large bouncer at the door, he checked his list, and we were granted entry. It took a second for my eyes to adjust to the lack of light. Once inside, I could see some of Los Angeles' richest and most powerful young Blacks. Some I recognized and others just looked somewhat familiar. Needless to say, all the beautiful people were in attendance. It was as if a royal decree had been issued. Anybody who was anybody was at the Olympic Connection that night. Shaq was easy enough to spot, heads above the majority of the other partygoers, who were gathered in the center of the club.

After glancing around the room, and allowing all the glitter to soak in for a minute, Deshawn and I began to circulate around the perimeters of the packed room. We hadn't inched our way around the wall very far when I heard a woman's voice screaming my name from across the room. It was Roxanne, a beautiful, black, high priced stripper, who was an acquaintance of mine. She signaled me to stay put and she would work her way over to me. Roxy emerged from the crowd with two black guys, wearing shades, in tow. The taller of the two men was introduced to me as Smiley. The shorter one with the dreadlocks was James. Roxy explained that these guys were friends of hers from Jamaica, who had a problem, and she knew I was just the man to solve it for them. She then quickly disappeared back into the crowd leaving me standing with Smiley and James. They were all decked out, with presidential Rolexes, diamonds and gold chains everywhere. I started making some small talk about New York and various places in Jamaica that I had visited. Almost in mid sentence, Smiley interrupted and said that they would like me to meet them for lunch tomorrow at their hotel to discuss business. With that he handed me his card, on which, he had scribbled his room number. I agreed to be there at 11:30 and they headed for the door. I guess the party was over as far as they were concerned. Deshawn and I stayed. We hooked up with some gorgeous women who entertained us until daylight. Fortunately I was able to meet Shaq that night. Deshawn managed to briefly introduce me to him. I was in awe by his tremendous size, but I did manage to thank him for a great party.

The next day I arrived at Smiley and James' hotel in Beverly Hills, and made my way up to their suite. I was right on time. When I think someone is trying to give me some of their money, I don't like to keep them waiting. James greeted me in his heavy Jamaican accent. He was still wearing his shades. "Eh mon, come on in." Smiley offered me a drink, which I declined. I never drink when discussing business. Not wanting to cloud my mind, I asked for a Coke instead. Smiley nodded and phoned our drink order down to room service, along with a platter of shrimp. It all sounded good to me. We sat outside on the balcony sipping our drinks and eating some of the biggest and freshest shrimp I had ever seen. We discussed Shaq's party and all of the gorgeous women in attendance before we got down to business.

I never did find out what sort of business Smiley and James were in. They thought I already knew. All I did know was that you don't ask too many questions. I could only deduct from their dress and demeanor that they might be involved in some sort of drug cartel, but who knows for sure.

James told me that he wanted to buy fifty or more of the most sophisticated, top of the line, computers in order to automate their organization. He wanted me to create an encryption software program for each one. I told him that it would be a piece of cake, but why stop there. I had been working on a set up to install external cameras (this was before external cameras were inexpensive) to a printer port and if I could sell them on the idea I could sweeten my bottom line by another 30 percent - at least.

When it comes to dollars and cents I'm a natural born salesman. I'm kind of like a dog that won't give up on his bone. I then began leading them down the path to my riches. I suggested for an additional $300 dollars, that I would install a wide-angle camera to each computer and they could place one at each of their locations. This way, they could watch anybody who was handling money or merchandise. The employees could be monitored at anytime, and from anyplace in the world. This idea really caught James and Smiley's attention. You could almost see the wheels turning in their heads. I continued to explain how my system would allow them to log on to any computer or laptop, and visually watch anything that was going on at any one location, at anytime. Even if they were cruising 35,000 feet over the Atlantic, or having dinner at their favorite restaurant down the street. They would be able to check up on their employees from anywhere. They were sold, but I couldn't stop there. I had to up the ante one more time. Almost jokingly I said, "Suppose I could set up a device to your system which would allow you to dial a number and have the system instantly burn down at any location. While you're somewhere else, say Brazil, eating Paella?" James quickly replied, "Why the fuck would I want to burn down one of my own places Mon?" For a brief second I thought I'd gone too far, maybe they weren't in the drug business after all. Time to set the hook a little deeper before he spit it out and I lose him completely. I had to think fast. I said, "Imagine for a minute someone who is involved in drugs or some other illegal activity, like gun running, and the ATF or DEA is hot on their trail. Say someone just snitches them out and they are out of the country at the time. What can they do to keep all of their records out of the DEA's reach? A smart person could view the whole proceedings live from a remote location. If that person decided he wanted to destroy all of the evidence before the DEA agents broke down the door, he could. This could be accomplished by dialing a phone number. Forty seconds later all of the incriminating evidence would be engulfed in flames."

I still did not know what their business was, but my scenario struck a cord with Smiley and James. It was obvious from their smiles that they were excited and anxious. The only thing James wanted to know was how soon could I have this system set up and installed. At that moment I knew it was payday for me. Most people want to know the bottom line first, not the installation date.

I told them I could have them up and running in less than three weeks. They seemed genuinely pleased. I let them know that I would need the usual 50% up front before I could start. "No problem mon," said James. "We'll have it to you within 48 hours. Cash if that's OK?" That's what I like about doing business with people of this caliber. Every deal they do is strictly in cash, no paper trails or taxes to contend with.

I quickly calculated that my cost would be approximately $1,200 dollars per computer. I figured I needed about 84 computers, 1 PC Anywhere software, 84 Mini cameras with wide-angle lenses, 84 cell phones with modem adapters, and a portable electrical outlet for continual use. I would also need a couple spools of wire, and 84 pagers to complete the system. I had quoted the Jamaican's $450,000 dollars for the entire job. That meant after expenses, I would clear nearly $300,000 dollars.

After completing my shopping list I went down to the local Hi-Tech Hustler spot where you can order any and everything, credit card numbers, cloned cell phones, computers, big screen televisions, and even night vision goggles. It was one stop shopping, I ordered just about everything I needed for the job except for the cell phones. I could not use cloned cell phones because they could not receive incoming calls and I could not take a chance that they would be disconnected in 30 days. If they were disconnected and the Jamaicans couldn't call in to terminate all of their spots like I promised, I would be hanging out with Elvis today. So I brought a credit profile of 20 people with super credit and went to a friend's home whom worked for LA Cellular to setup the accounts.

Two weeks later, after receiving all of my components, I began setting them up. The first location I was to set up was in a high-rise office near the Trade Center in New York City. I hooked up the computer, the screen, and then plugged in the mini cameras into the panel port of the computer. Next I plugged the cell phone into the modem and wall outlet. Everything was in place except for the detonating device and the explosives. These items were to be left up to Smiley and James. They placed them in an adjoining bathroom under the sink. My D-Day device was about as simple in theory as it gets. All it involved was 5 gallons of gasoline, a stick of dynamite, some wire and a pager. I converted the pager to emit a small electrical charge when it was called. Two wires came from the pager and this is where my part ended. The connection to the explosives was left to the Jamaicans, not that I didn't think it would work, I just did not want to get involved in burning something down, especially this multi million dollar building or myself.

I had previously demonstrated my D-Day device for Smiley and James out in a Southern California desert and it worked perfectly. James was so impressed he wanted to know if such a device could be installed in a car's gas tank. I told him that I didn't see why it couldn't but I really did not want to know anymore. After several other installations on the east coast, my next stop was in a large mid western city. I was instructed to go to a warehouse near the old stockyards in an almost abandoned neighborhood. Smiley was already there and he let me right in. Once inside we walked through the dark and nearly vacant warehouse to an abandoned office in the back. There at a long table were six or seven men sitting around in nothing but their skivvies and wearing white protective paper masks. It was a sight to behold. The men barely glanced up at me. They just continued weighing and bagging up some white powdery substance that was packaged in the center of the table.

Smiley pointed across the room to an old beat up desk and said, "Go ahead and set it up over there mon." I really didn't like the looks of this place but I didn't let on. I hurried and set up the computer system in record time. I then packed up my tools and the rest of my stuff and high tailed it out of there. While I was leaving, Smiley was connecting the gasoline and dynamite to the two wires that I had left dangling from the pager. The camera and computers were already up and running. James O.K.'d the installation from another location. I didn't catch my breath until I was safely back in my hotel room. I kept thinking what would have happened if the cops burst in while I was doing the installation. I hated the idea of doing time for a crime I didn't commit. Drugs just aren't my bag.

My next job was back in Southern California. This time it was in one of those construction trailers inside a chain link fence with a bunch of tractor-trailers parked along the side. It appeared to be a legitimate trucking operation. I installed the computer system and camera. Then I left them the wired pager. I made sure that all of my jobs were wiped clean of any fingerprints. I told the guy in the trailer that Smiley would be by in a few days to finish the job and hook up the pager.

The rest of the installations took me back to the Midwest, and down to Texas. It didn't usually take me much more than a half an hour to set up each place. The worst part of the job was the traveling time involved in getting to each of the locations. Luckily, I didn't have to go to any more counting houses like the one near the stockyards. Most of the locations appeared to be legitimate.

When I finished my part of the deal, which was just a few set ups, James had something extra for me. He setup a meeting for me in a warehouse near Los Angeles Airport. Here, using visual aids, I conducted a class in the basics of computer operation to about fifty of James's employees.

James was as happy as a clam with his new computer system, which he could monitor from his laptop anywhere in the world. He loved switching back and forth through all his 84 different locations and just watching his employees making money for him. After all of the systems were up and running I received the balance they owed me in cash.

I didn't hear from either Smiley or James for almost eight months after that. Then one day, out of the blue, James called. "Say mon, one of my cameras are down and no one knows how to fix it. All you can see is static and lines across the screen. I think we need a new camera." He continued, "I wouldn't ask but it's one of my key locations and I think there's a fox in the hen house, you know what I mean mon?" Reluctantly I agreed to fly out and check it out. I was prepared to install a new camera if necessary. I knew I didn't have any other choice. When he told me it was the location at the warehouse near the stockyards, I tried real hard to back out. I had vowed never to go back to that place again, but James was more than convincing:

"You're the only one we can trust mon, if I sent anyone else in there we couldn't afford to let them leave, you know what I mean Mon?" How could I say no?

I caught a flight that afternoon and had a taxi take me directly from the airport to the warehouse. I told the driver to keep the meter running. I didn't want to be there any longer than need be. I had purchased a new camera on my way to LAX and my plan was to just remove and replace the old camera and get the hell out of there. I had to knock and wait several minutes before someone finally opened the warehouse door and let me in. Once again we walked across the concrete floor in the near dark to the back office. On this day there were only two men present. There was the guy who let me in and a guy busy on the desk computer. The long table was bare except for a couple of commercial type scales that stood motionless. I took out my tools and the new camera from my carry on bag and quickly got to work. I had the old camera off and the new one up and working in about five minutes. I told them that my taxi's meter was running and I quickly made my way to the door. The guy that had let me in unlocked the numerous deadbolts and I was back on the street and in my taxi.

It was almost dark by then, but from the refuge of the taxi I spotted what appeared to be two police officers in an unmarked car about half way down the block from the warehouse. The officers made eye contact with me as my taxi drove past them. I thought I was really fucked. From where they were parked, there was no way they hadn't seen me enter the warehouse with my carry on bag. As we drove on, I kept my eye on the unmarked cruiser, but for some unknown reason they never even tried to intercept my taxi. They just stayed parked where they were. Once out of view of the cruiser I redirected my attention to the front. Coming down the street were four cop cars and what looked like a swat type of vehicle. My heart was pounding up in my throat and I thought I would shit my pants. As they sped past us heading toward the warehouse, none of them even glanced in our direction. I returned my attention again to the rear window as the parade of police vehicles pulled in front of the warehouse. As we rounded the corner towards the tollway, I could see a flash of light and a burst of flames emanating toward the darkened sky.

I told the cabby there would be an extra C note in it if he could get me to the airport post haste. I couldn't stop shaking or looking over my shoulder till the plane started taxiing down the runway. Once in the air I put on my headphones and reclined in my seat. I closed my eyes and thanked my maker. In another three hours I would be back home free and safe in the arms of the woman I loved. With that I drifted off to sleep to the drone of the airplanes engines thinking that I really had to quit fucking around with these drug people.

New Policy Changes

It is not just the organization and I. Thousands of other Hi-Tech Hustlers around the world have hit so many companies so hard and for so much money, they had to change the way they do business.

1. AT&T: They use to allow anyone to call in and order an 800 number. All you had to do was give any bogus name and address and your number would work within 24 hours. Well, after I personally hit them for 300 numbers and $7.4 million dollars you can't do that anymore.

2. GTE Paging, MobileCom and Pagenet: They used to allow a person to order pagers without doing a credit check and with no money up front. Well after I scored 800 pagers and $600,000 dollars in three weeks, they changed that.

3. CompuServe: Would allow you to log on and do your banking. After a $200,000 dollar loss in five weeks they stopped that.

4. Imgram Micro, Mersiel, and Tech Data: They would give a $2,500 to $5,000 dollar credit line instantly to all new vendors. Not anymore.

5. Bank Of America: Used to allow you to make a deposit in the ATM and with draw $300 dollars instantly. Not anymore.

6. 1-800-Collect and 1-800-Call ATT: Used to allow you to bill to a third party without any verification. Well, after $2 million dollars in losses in 30 days, guess what, not anymore.

7. Compaq Computer: Used to give you a $1,500 dollar in instant credit for new customers writing checks for products when you order direct from Compaq. By the way this book was written on a Compaq.

8. Alliance of Dallas Texas: They were the #1 distributor for Dialogic a company that sells high tech digital voice cards at $5,000 dollars a pop. They use to let you write a check or purchase orders for all new customers. After 100 Dialogic SC-TI cards worth $500,000 dollars in a year, all that changed.

Hide The Duckets!

After I found out my crimey snitched me out (That would be Otto Lamont Beasley), the judge who was presiding over my pre-trial offered me my first deal. She would let me out that night for thirty days and I was to come back with a $100,000 dollar cashiers check. I would either get out on probation or get out in ten years. When my lawyer presented me with this deal, my response to that deal was hell no. I know a setup when I hear one. This was what they really wanted me to do. They wanted to let me out that night so I would have the lawyers for AT&T, the private detectives for Pagenet, Motorola, and GTE, along with the San Bernardino Police Department, FBI, and the IRS eating donuts and drinking coffee wondering where in the world was I going to get the $100,000 dollars from. I would have been under more surveillance than the president. I was born at night but not last night. No deal.

People in my business have the same problem criminals (which I am not) have - unverifiable income. If you made a million dollars in illegal transactions you can't put that on a W2 or 1099. If you put that money in your bank account here in the Untied States, the I.R.S. will be all over you. Your only option is to open an offshore bank account.

A CEO once hired me to hack into his company and crash the accounting computers the day before an IRS audit because he was really stealing from the company and it's shareholders. He wanted to transfer my fee to an offshore account, and if I didn't have one he will have one set up for me. I was only 23 years old, I didn't know what an offshore account was. He sat me down and explained the whole thing. He told me that these accounts were more expensive to open than a regular bank account in the United States, but since I was making over six figures for the job that wasn't a problem. The cost started at $20,000 dollars for the best account. It was like buying fire insurance for your home. It is of no use to you until your house burns down. The basic thrust is to put assets out of the reach of futures creditors. If you wait to be sued or audited by the IRS, a judge can declare it invalid.

The process to set up an account is simple. First, find a good attorney that specializes in asset protection. There are a lot of assets protection trust companies that can help you set a do-it-yourself version for as little as $150 dollars. You get what you pay for. Second, find a good spot. Two of the major hot spots for offshore trusts are the Cook Islands off the coast of New Zealand, and the Cayman Islands. Cook Island laws were written by attorneys from the U.S. and are among the worlds most flexible and liberal toward debtors. The Cayman Islands have built a reputation as an ideal offshore haven over the years. Even though their laws are not necessarily the strongest. I personally like the Cayman Island accounts because they set you up with an account number and a password. No one could ever get into it without the number and password. Many countries have anti-coercion laws that prohibit trustees from releasing any of your assets to foreign courts. That includes any American ones that have sought an order to seize your savings. If you are really looking for a place that's really going to welcome your offshore trust, try Liechtenstein. It's a tiny country on the border of Austria and Switzerland. In order to tear down any of the walls the country let you put up to protect your money, someone would have to find an attorney who could argue the case in German.

Since the government doesn't let attorneys work on contingency basis, a creditor would have to come up with the cash to pay a lawyer up front. If someone did win a case against you, he couldn't collect any punitive damages, because Liechtenstein doesn't allow it. If the case were lost, he would be obliged to pay your legal fees. If that isn't enough of an obstacle course, you can order trustee's to shift your money to a friendly place if it comes under attack. Your trust could be hopping around the globe with major creditors chasing it. One thing I have learned to do is never show how much money you have in the bank. I keep enough to pay a few bills but that's it. I bounce checks on purpose to throw off the peeking eyes.

Remember, when you deposit $10,000 dollars or more in your account at one time a flag is sent to the IRS. If you decide to buy a home or an expensive car that you cannot have your name associated with, hire an attorney to purchase it under the name of an offshore corporation. You then rent the property from the offshore corporation for a dollar, or a thousand dollars. Make sure your name is not on the corporation papers. Most importantly, never trust anybody with information to your account. Not your mother, father, brother, sister, no one!! Why? You'll get screwed every time if you do.

Easy Money

Most people are more inclined to guard their credit card numbers more than they will protect their checkbooks. People are lulled into a false sense of security with checks. Rationalizing that it would take an expert forger to duplicate their signatures. They don't even consider the importance of their account numbers.

I'm sure most of you have been at a store at one time and have made an error when writing out a check. What do you do? Do you write void across the face of the check, or do you rip up the check and toss it in the trash? Either way, you might as well just write out a blank check and hand it over to a complete stranger. In this day and age, you don't need a gun and a mask to rob a bank, all you need is an account number. When I was sixteen years old, and a sophomore in high school, I received a trial offer from an Internet service called CompuServe. After logging onto my computer with all my personal information, and coming up with a temporary user name and private password, I was then asked by CompuServe how I wanted to pay for future billing? I was given the option of paying with a credit card number or check free. Needless to say, I didn't have a credit card, nor did I have access to one, so that option was out of the question. The only alternative left was check free. Although I didn't have a clue to what check free was I selected it. I was then asked to type in all the numbers from the bottom of my checks. Well shit, I didn't have a checking account either, and I wasn't about to use my parent's numbers. It's one thing to screw strangers or people you dislike, but I would never screw my family or friends.

I wasn't about to accept defeat in my quest to get on line with an Internet service. I took this minor set back as a challenge. All I needed was a checking account number and I would be back in business. After giving the situation some thought I came up with the perfect solution. I had this bitchy accounting teacher who had announced on the first day of class, "I do not give A's in my class." Because of her irreverent attitude towards her students, I would make her my target. In my juvenile reasoning mind, I had rationalized that I would be doing my fellow classmates a favor. The next day, I arrived at school early and began to enact my plan. I made sure no one was in or around the classroom when I entered. I went straight to the bottom left hand desk drawer where I knew Ms. Ashley kept her purse. Sure enough, her brown handbag was just where I expected it to be. As I was rifling through her purse, I came across Ms. Ashley's birth control pills. The idea of this underweight, dogged faced bitch having some poor asshole sticking his face between her legs about made me puke.

Finally I came across her checkbook. It was in one of those vinyl covers that came free with a box of checks. I thought to myself "God, this woman really doesn't have any class." Still justifying in my mind the act I was about to commit, I carefully removed the last check in the sequence, figuring it would be awhile before the bitch even realized that the check was even missing. I then checked her balance. As expected her check register looked like it came out of an accounting textbook. All the numbers were neatly aligned in the proper columns.

Later that day, I had Ms. Ashley's accounting class. After I had violated the woman's second most personal possession, her purse, I had difficulty making eye contact with her. It seemed like the longest class period of my high school career.

I could hardly wait for the school day to be over, so I could race home and log back on the computer. Only this time, I could finally get on the Internet where a whole new world awaited me.

Later that evening, after supper and my parents had retired to the other end of the house, I logged on to Compu-Serve. Once again I went through the sign up procedure, but this time I changed some of the personal information to cover my tracks. I then selected my private password. I chose 'Easy Money'. It seemed appropriate; after all, that's what I figured Ms. Ashley's check was to me. When I got to the part about check free or credit card, I whipped out the folded check from the depths of my wallet. With the next click of the mouse it asked me to enter the name, address, and account number, then the bank routing number from the bottom left hand side of the check. When I completed those instructions, the screen automatically brought up the name and address printed on the check and then asked me if all the information was correct and up to date. I confirmed that everything was correct on the check, but the mailing address was different than the residence address shown on the check. I then typed in an address and apartment number from the area projects just a few blocks away. I was certain some of those fat welfare mothers wouldn't take the time to write ' return to sender' on the mail. Again CompuServe took the pertinent information and no further questions were asked.

After about ten minutes worth of work, if you could call it work, I was a full-fledged member of CompuServe. The door was now open to me, and the world was about to be mine. Little did anyone know, but they had just let the bull out into the pasture with the cows, and I was about to fuck over everybody I could with my new CompuServe account.

For obvious reasons, I am not going to tell you exactly how I did this, but around midnight; I typed, 'go bank' into the computer. I figured I needed an exact balance to Ms. Ashley's account. Just to make sure. Ms. Ashley's bank and its address appeared on screen, and with another click of the mouse, the current balance materialized. She had $2,553.69 in her checking account. Not bad for a teacher I thought. My juvenile mind didn't even consider that this might be her whole savings, or even that she might have a mortgage payment due later in the month. To me it was free and easy money.

I was like a drunken sailor on leave. I logged on to an online shopping network and began to do my damage. I bought myself some new expensive threads, some computer games, and hardware. I had it all shipped to a private postal box a homie of mine had set up for just this sort of scams. After the spending spree high had worn off, I began to feel a slight remorse for Ms. Ashley. It passed shortly. I clicked over a few more sites until I reached a florist and I decided to order Ms. Ashley the biggest and almost the most expensive floral arrangement they offered. After all, it was her money, and she deserved it. It would be little consolation after she realized her account had been cleaned out. But when she received the flowers with a card reading "From one of your admirers" she could not help but be flattered. It would certainly make her day, just like the easy money had made my day.

Back in those days, about the only thing you could do with a checking account on the Internet was to purchase items. Today, with that same information from a checking account, you could have the money transferred to another account or even pay gas, electric, or phone bills online. The mark will probably have a harder time convincing their bank that they didn't transfer money or make purchases out of their checking account than proving a fraudulent credit card transaction.

So the next time you're writing a check wherever it may be, just keep in mind that, the young guy behind the register you just handed your check over to, may have read this book, and just might be your next banker.

A New World Order

I'm not a psychic, but I can predict what is going to happen within the next ten years in the technology world. I guarantee that every one of the following statements will happen and I have set it up as a checklist so you can check each one off as it happens:

☐ There will be two types of people: Computer literate people and computer dummies. Race will have nothing to do with an individual's success. It will be based on the ability to program C++, or design a Fiber Optic Network.

☐ There will be 300 out of 400 people featured in Forbes 400 richest people that have work in the technology information field. This field includes: television, Internet services, Internet stores, computers, software, multi-media service, satellites, robotics, technology manufacturing, computer aided design, and telecommunications. Long distance companies will start to be replaced by Internet phone companies.

☐ You will no longer pay per minute charges. Instead, a flat rate for unlimited use will be offered. Calls will not go through conventional phone lines but will be carried over digital lines leading into the Internet.

☐ Traditional department stores will be selling more products and services online than in their retail stores.

☐ Everyone will have one personal phone number that will also be his or her fax number, modem number, cellular number, Internet number, and pager number. Pagers will be two-way pagers. No need to go to a phone to reply to a pager, you will be able to respond through a little keyboard on the pager. Your pager will also receive faxes on the LCD display.

☐ Video game characters will be replaced with real people as characters.

☐ Every rapist, child molester, or violent criminal that gets released from prison will where an ankle bracelet that will let police know their whereabouts all over the world. If the police are in pursuit of a suspect, they will have the ability to send an electric shock through the bracelet that would put the criminal unconscious for at least fifteen minutes.

☐ Bank robberies by computer hackers will be up 50%.

☐ More consumers will have their credit cards abused from doing business on the Internet than in the entire history of credit card fraud.

☐ The same way the United States started the FBI to combat organized crime; a new international crime division will be created out of NATO members to combat international computer crimes.

☐ Wars and conflicts will be fought via the computer. Governments will have an elite group of computer hackers with the ability to control computers, destroy financial information, intercept passwords, destroy medical information, intercept bank transfers, shut down foreign air traffic control, shut down utility companies, and destroy all birth certificate records. What this crack team of computer hackers could do is unlimited.

☐ You will be able to obtain a Bachelor's, Master's, or Doctorate Degree via the Internet from several major Universities.

◻ Companies will request more people who are Microsoft Certified Engineers than people holding Bachelor degrees in computer science.

◻ You will be able to watch made for Internet movies and concerts. It will have all the major movie stars or Grammy award performers.

◻ Your kids will be replacing school notebooks with palm top computers.

◻ Online gambling will be legalized over the Internet.

◻ A storage device the size of a credit card will be created to store our credit reports, medical history, criminal history (if any), and driving record. It may even work as a regular credit card or ATM card.

◻ Instead of having to use a code, home security systems will be able to recognize your voice, thumb, body motion, or even your retina. Televisions will be controlled by voice. You'll be able to say, "Turn to channel four and record HBO at eight p.m."

◻ The more sophisticated computers get the more sophisticated criminal activities will become. Even though the government changed our paper money making it harder to counterfeit, criminals with high resolution scanners, color printers, and color copiers will be able to duplicate currency so well the treasury department will have problems telling the real from fake.

☐ The display on your cellular phone will be able to do video conferencing.

☐ Microsoft will still dominate the software industry.

☐ I will be one of the most powerful innovators in the telephony (computer communications) industry.

A Dance With The Devil

My mother had two sons. Bringing us up in the projects was no easy task for even the strongest black woman. Every day mama reminded us that there was another life outside the ghetto. Through all her preaching, she managed to get at least one of us into a prestigious university. Unlike my brother, I chose a different path, one that seemed to promise glamour, power, and wealth, but would eventually land me in jail.

I could have gone to Howard, Grambling, USC, or maybe even MIT, but I was sucked into the idea of fast money. The philosophy of the streets told me to live for today, screw tomorrow. I figured if I skipped college, I could start my high technology company right after high school. Four years later, my classmates who went to college would be competing with each other for positions in my company. Why work your way up the ladder, when you could start at the top? From the desolation of the projects, I could see my way out.

Most of my homies in the hood wanted to deal drugs or play in the NBA. I had a different dream. I wanted to own a telephone company. They only wanted to be HNIC (head nigga in charge), I was going to be CEO. Seldom did any of my homies ever get past HNIC. And a professional sports team never recruited any of them. I, on the other hand, realized my dream of becoming CEO of my own communications corporation. As short-lived as it was, I did live the dream and experience the perks that came with it.

I craved respect, but not just from the people in the ghetto. I wanted respect from blacks and whites, rich and poor. I wanted respect from the streets of Harlem to the hills of the Silicon Valley. With money and power I assumed respect would automatically follow. I would do anything to get it. I would lie, cheat, steal, and if necessary, kill for money, power, and respect. But I didn't want to go the traditional route.

My school was the University of the Streets. My professors were successful hustlers. From Crenshaw Boulevard to Wall Street I learned my lessons from watching the street wise. From Nicky Barnes, a big time drug dealer from Harlem to Michael Millikin, the junk bond king who paid his $900 million dollar fine in cash. Movies like The Godfather, Scarface, New Jack City, and Gotti reinforced my notions of get-rich-quick and live the good life.

It seemed a real possibility and for a while I lived the dream. It was a world where Moet flowed from bottles like water from a fountain. All my luxury cars sat on 20-inch chrome rims. Rolexes decorated my wrist like cuff links.

My feet wore the skins of endangered reptiles. I wore at least $20,000 dollars worth of jewelry at all times, from diamond bracelets to a five-carat diamond earring. When I paid cash for a car that cost four times my parents salary, I knew I'd finally made it. With brand new fifty and hundred dollar bills I honed my skills of making paper airplanes. My date gasped in horror the day I lit her Cuban cigar with a crisp C note. I loved it. Cell phones chimed like a well-orchestrated symphony. I had a private jet standing by 24 hours a day to take me anywhere my greedy heart desired. On a whim I could jet off to Bay Harbor, to dine on live Maine lobster. I'd catch a Knicks game at the Garden, seated behind Spike Lee. God I miss those days.

It was the epitome of materialism. Conspicuous consumption really attracted the ladies. But except for a few, they were only showpieces to me. Women were on my arm only to compliment me, just like the accents of my jewelry complimented my Armani suit. It's amazing I didn't draw more attention from the authorities in those days.

I thought it was the American Dream come true. In fact I was just living in a dream world. Just like in the movies. I saw myself as a Tony Montana or Nino Brown. The difference was unlike the actors who played them on the screen, when the final scene came down and the director yelled, "cut!" I didn't get to go home. Instead I got a "Go

To Jail" card. I didn't pass go. I didn't collect my two hundred dollars.

All my life, and especially in jail, I've heard people say it's the White man keeping me down. It's easy enough for a black man to fall for that one. But I know it wasn't a White man who gave me a laptop and a cellular phone and said, "Go steal." Most of my customers were rich white men who represent white-owned corporations, but I can't blame them. Nor do I blame my parents or the way I was raised. I could blame TV or rap music, but I don't.

The choice was my own. I could have dragged my ass off to college like other bright young men. I could have started at the bottom of the ladder and worked my way to the top, one step at a time. "You gotta crawl before you can walk," my mother used to tell me. But I let greed become my Holy Spirit. Instead of God, I worshipped cash. I knew it could buy what I craved.

The Promised Land wasn't to be found in the architectural starkness of the projects, but in the lushness of Brentwood and other parts of the almost exclusive White mans world. My ticket to the Promised Land would have to be paid for in cash. The show of wealth transported me from a poor Black man from the ghetto through the desert into the land of milk and honey. And it was first class all the way.

I knew right from wrong just like I knew day from night. I chose to ignore all that. In the pursuit of the almighty dollar, I had to take the fast track. Maybe some brothers are kept down by the White man, But me, I was just greedy and figured I could get what I wanted faster than anyone else. It wasn't that I was lazy and didn't want to work. In fact, I was driven by the greed. I often put in a fourteen-hour day and slept only when my eyes could no longer focus. Even then it was a struggle to sleep more than a few hours at a time.

Who do I blame? Who do you think? Let me tell you. I've danced with the devil, and let me tell you, the devil ain't White.

House Of Cards

In previous chapters, I have shared with you some of my exploits and high tech crimes I've taken part in. Now, as I sit here in the #6 South wing of the Los Angeles Federal Detention Center, waiting for, and negotiating my release, I keep reflecting back to the incidences that led up to my incarceration.

After the FBI raided my office and subsequently AT&T slapped a $24,000,000 million dollar lawsuit against me, all my working capital and assets were frozen. Any cash or property I had stashed, I couldn't access because the Fed's and AT&T were still looking for it. I was virtually broke, which was a predicament I wasn't accustomed to. Out of a sense of desperation to regain my financial status, I decided to rebuild my SkyMail Network System that I had sold a year or two before.

SkyMail was the most sophisticated voicemail system in the world. When you signed up with SkyMail we would give you a toll free 800 or 877 numbers that went directly into your voicemail system. The features of SkyMail consisted of selecting what languages you wanted your prompts to be in, such as English, French, Spanish, German, or Chinese. SkyMail allowed you to block a phone number or part of a phone number such as 909-555*. That way anyone calling you in the 909 area code who's phone number started with 555 would be notified that you do not except calls from that area. You could even block a whole area code. SkyMail also was the first system out there that allowed you to check your voicemail messages over the phone. Before two-way pagers were out, SkyMail would allow a person to leave a message in a SkyMail mailbox. The system would then allow the person to enter their pager number - even if it was with a different pager company - and the message was heard in the SkyMail mailbox. The system would even page that person back to let them know that their message was heard. One of the best features of SkyMail was that every person who called your SkyMail mailbox could get the phone number that they were calling from, even if they had call blocking. So if a person was calling from their home, work, or even a secret government office, their caller ID information was recorded. So when you heard the message it would then give you the area code and phone number of the person and even give you the option of dialing that number back. That's right, you could call your SkyMail mailbox and then place a call anywhere in the world that you wanted. If someone tried to call your SkyMail mailbox and hack in, SkyMail would page you and let you know someone was trying to get into your mailbox.

When you called your SkyMail mailbox a message would be waiting to let you know the area code and phone number and the numbers typed in while trying to hack your Sky-Mail mailbox. The greatest feature of all was that if you placed a call to someone using your SkyMail mailbox you could press the "*" key and it would then record everything that was said. It then would keep it in your voicemail for up to 30 days. What made SkyMail unique was that it worked with any pager on any paging network or no pager at all. It could even call you at home, on a cell phone or even in a hotel room to let you know that you have a message waiting. I could go on and on and on and on about the features but I think that should be enough to let you know how BAD (GOOD) I was to write that software and build the computers that ran it. All I needed was a little capital for my new business to get underway, and since I couldn't utilize my money, I needed someone else's money. That opportunity presented itself one night at a bachelor party for a friend of mine. As it so happened, that night I met Mr. Ben Garret. Mr. Garret was an unsophisticated man, but he seemed to be well off, and well connected. I suggested that we meet the next day at his office to discuss a business venture I thought he might be interested in.

The following day, Mr. Garret and I met as planned. I proposed to Mr. Garret that we start a corporation under the name of International Voice Mail Network. The company would be a California corporation consisting of about one million shares to be sold for one dollar per share. Mr. Garret would act as CEO, and I would act as President. As president, my duties would include being in charge of research and development. Mr. Garret would handle the finances. We would each receive 450,000 shares and the remaining 100,000 shares would be sold to outside investors. After signing the necessary agreements, between Mr. Garret and myself, we filed the paperwork for our new corporation. I was back in business doing what I do best, making money.

It wasn't very long after Mr. Garret and I started our partnership, that I realized he just didn't have much of a business sense. Most of the potential investors he brought in didn't have the money he'd claimed they had. I don't think we sold more that 30,000 shares out of the original 100,000 shares we'd set up to be used as working capital. I found myself having to dip into my own hidden stashes just to meet payroll and other office expenses. Before I knew it, I had used about $50,000 dollars out of my own pocket. It wasn't part of my plan to bankroll this operation.

One day, I received a call from Andrea, my former bookkeeper, who worked for me prior to the FBI Raid. Andrea told me that she had a friend who owned a pager shop called Pager Depot. The guy wanted to sell some of his national pager customers for $30 dollars a piece to raise some money. I knew things were about to turn around for International Voice Mail Network. I initially agreed to purchase 15,000 customers and an additional 30,000 more if 90% stayed with the service for over a month's time. As I was negotiating the final deal with Andrea's friend, I got a call from another long time so-called homie of mine named Wallace Allen. Wallace usually called only when he needed something. This time was no different. Wallace's newest venture was a local newspaper called 'The West Side Story'. He and his failing paper needed a loan. From past experience, I knew it would be difficult for Wallace to pay back any loan, regardless of the amount. So instead, I offered to hire him to process the credit card billing for the new customers I had just purchased. I offered him 5% of the monthly billing. Wallace was so pleased by our arrangement that he signed up as a SkyMail dealer and even advertised the service in his weekly newspaper. I knew Wallace wasn't always above board in his business dealings, but in the past he'd always been straightforward with me. After all he was the Godfather to both of my sons. When I put Wallace in charge of credit card billing, I didn't realize how much he had gone into debt with his paper and how desperate he was for money. Once Wallace received the accounts I had faxed to him, he began to double and even triple the billings. What Wallace was doing was taking a credit card number under the name of John Smith and running it under Jonathan Smith. He would then process the card through his newspaper and keep the money.

Each of these sales needed a SkyMail account and an activated pager. The following day, I began working on obtaining the pagers for each of the accounts I had purchased. Pagenet was more than willing to lease me 175 activated pagers for the mere sum of $500 dollars. It was that simple. I gave Pagenet a check and they delivered the pagers the next day and we were in business. We immediately began to set up SkyMail accounts for all of our customers and started to Fed-Ex the pagers to customers all around the country.

A few weeks later, customers were calling us and complaining that they had never ordered any pagers. We explained to them that we had bought out Pager Depot along with their accounts. These customers claimed that they had never heard of Pager Depot, and they hadn't ordered, nor did they want the Pagers. After about a dozen or so of those types of calls, I knew that the hustler got hustled. I was devastated that my trusted friend Andrea, who was like a Sister to me, set me up with a guy who sold phony accounts. I had been duped along with the innocent credit card holders. The only one that came out on top was Wallace. Within the week, the majority of the pagers had been returned, and the business was spiraling rapidly into debt to the tune of about $12,000 dollars a week. Normally I would consider it chump change, but it was my own personal funds, not Mr. Garret's or even the shareholders that bankrolled the deal. To make matters worse, payroll was due the next day, which was supposed to be Mr. Garret's responsibility. Previously I had always made payroll from my own stash, but by now I was fed up bankrolling this venture only to share future profits with Mr. Garret and the other shareholders.

When I contacted Mr. Garret at his office, to give him the payroll amount, I knew just what his response would be, "I don't have it". I then explained to him, if he didn't come up with the payroll by tomorrow, I would be forced to shut down the entire operation. With that, our conversation ended abruptly.

Unbeknown to me, Lamont, my number man, had been eavesdropping outside of my office doorway and immediately jumped to the conclusion that payroll was not going to be made. Not only was he not going to get paid, but he was going to lose his job too. Lamont decided to take matters into his own hands by collecting the returned pagers in the mailroom and he resold them. Somehow Lamont unloaded the pagers at a local pager store for about $50 dollars a piece.

It was shortly before closing time, as I sat at my desk wondering if Mr. Garret would come through or if I had to make payroll once again out of my own pocket when Lamont burst in with a fat envelope in hand. Lamont slapped the envelope on my desktop and slid it in my direction. "Hey man," Lamont said, "check that out." I picked up the envelope and peered inside at the stack of hundred dollar bills. "Shit man, where did you get all that cash?" I asked. He said, "Before you go ballistic on me, just listen, I've got a sweet deal for you." Lamont went on to explain how he'd gotten the wad of cash and how he had overheard my call to Mr. Garret. Lamont went on to say, while he was trying to locate someone to unload our pagers, he had made a contact that had wanted 100,000, preferably the new Motorola two-way, pagers. I was still upset with Lamont for selling something that was not his. He could have at least checked it out with me. And I really didn't see the relevance of his so-called contact. After all, I was in the voice-mail business, not the pager business. Lamont could tell by the grimace on my face that he needed to unfold his entire plan. He stated that he knew a way to acquire pagers in quantities of 100, which we could sell to our contact for a large profit and make a bundle of money in a month's time.

A smile started to come over my face. Money always makes me smile. He'd peaked my interest with the six-figure number in 30 days. I needed to know how. Lamont said he'd checked around with several major pager companies like GTE, Pagenet, and Skytel, and found out that we could get pagers by just paying for airtime. That way we could sell the pagers and take a portion of the money to pay the billing at the end of the month. "Why would we pay the bill?" I asked. Lamont replied, "Because we are going to get insurance on each pager which will cover theft. Once we fulfill our order for 100,000 pagers, we will report the pagers stolen and the insurance will cover it." By the time Lamont finished explaining his plan, I was totally sold on the idea. We could get the pagers for no money down. We would have to pay for the insurance however. We'd make the money by selling them to our Asian contact for cash. Then we'd call the police and report them stolen, turn in the Police report to the pager company, and walk away with pure profit. Being the greedy S.O.B. that I am, I said, "Let's do it." Within a week's time, Lamont delivered to me the first installment of the deal. His plan had worked! In fact it worked so well, that we went out and purchased matching new Lincoln Navigators.

Back in 1998, Lamont was just a nineteen-year-old kid that was now rolling in dough. He invested in a failing night club called The Pink Cadillac and turned it into Chocolate City, which became quite a prosperous club for young Blacks. Lamont wasn't even old enough to get into his own club. I on the other hand, being older and a bit wiser than my counter part Lamont, tried not to draw attention to my newfound wealth through conspicuous consumption.

Our new pager scam was about to phase out, but then all good things must come to an end. Anyway, we'd made a good living off of it and it was time to move on to something else. Arriving at my office one morning I was greeted by some message slips on my desk. They were from several of the pager companies we were dealing with. I felt tightness in my throat. Was the jig finally up? After giving the matter some thought, I convinced myself that if we had been caught, they wouldn't be leaving messages. They would have turned the whole thing over to the cops. I called the first pager company back to see what the problem was. To my surprise, the agent on the other end of the phone told me that they had a couple of checks signed by Lamont Beasley that hadn't cleared. It didn't make sense at first, but when they told me that the checks had been drawn against the First National Bank of New York, suddenly all the pieces fell together. Those were old checks from an account that had been closed about four years prior. I had stored the checks in a box in the closet of my office. I returned a few more calls, and received the same story from the rest of the pager companies. It doesn't take a genius to figure out that Lamont had been snooping around my office and found the checkbook. But why, when I had been giving him cash to pay the bills to the pager companies? Why was he writing bad checks? Now the pager companies were demanding their pagers be returned by Monday, or they were going to have to press charges against us with the police. I was livid when I yelled to my secretary in the outer office. "Tell Lamont to get his fucking ass in here now!" Moments later, Lamont sheepishly stuck his head in my door and said, "Sup boss?" This was neither the first or the last time Lamont was to suffer the consequences of my anger. "What the fuck were you thinking Lamont?" I screamed in his face. Lamont didn't even have a chance to explain himself as I continued my tirades of insults and threatening gestures. Finally I told him to get the hell out of my office. I was so pissed that I didn't even want to look at him. I told him I'd talk to him first thing tomorrow morning after I had time to think things over. I was just trying to regain my composure when I received more bad news. Not only did Lamont write checks on a closed account, he'd also written Skymail checks all over town and had kept the cash I had given him to pay for those items.

I knew now what I was going to have to do. I was going to have to get rid of Lamont. He was no longer an asset. He was a liability. He was single handedly tearing down our house of cards and we were all in jeopardy. The only problem was that how do you get rid of a person who was deep into my underworld business without him dropping a dime on me. Lamont could blackmail me or even become a competitor to me. I realistically did not think he was smart enough to do either.

I decided to put the whole day behind me and accept a dinner invitation from a lady friend named Rohana. She wanted to come over to my place and cook for me. We watched the season finale of Seinfeld on my big screen TV. It sure beat sitting around stewing over the day's events. I knew I had to fire Lamont in the morning.

I was feeling much more relaxed after a couple hours of sex with Rohana and then a good nights sleep. As I was pulling up to the office around 8:50am that Friday I noticed that there wasn't anyone on the street. No buses, cabs, cars or people walking around. I found that very odd. San Bernardino always has some activity going on downtown. I arrived in the office and found Lamont waiting outside my office door. I didn't feel like getting my blood pressure up so I told him to wait in his office and I will call him when I am ready. I walked into my office trying not to get worked up. I sat behind my desk and logged on to my computer. As I was checking my email I was looking out the window still noticing that there is no activity downtown. I am still thinking to myself something odd is going on. Not more than three minutes later I heard shouting from my employees and different voices screaming down, down, down. As I stood up to go see what the commotion was about I noticed numerous red dots on my silk tie and chest. As I looked up I saw men with automatic weapons wearing black ski mask and black jackets screaming, "Get your hands in the air!" My first thought was that I was getting robbed, when I heard a voice a familiar voice that said, "Mr. Evans your under arrest." I then saw a tall 6'5", stocky man in a cheap suit who I recognized as DICKtective Jones. This is the same DICKtective who has been trying to get me in handcuffs for almost 7 years. He said to me, "Mr. Evans you're under arrest." The first thing out of my mouth was "State or Feds?" I knew I had done so much shit over the past few years, that I didn't know just what offense I was being arrested for, or by whom. Was it the local police, FBI, IRS, FCC, or maybe even Interpol? DICKtective Jones informed me that he'd been watching my dealings for sometime, and was just waiting for me to slip up. DICKtective Jones began to read my Miranda rights to me as he slapped on the handcuffs. The cuffs were so tight around my wrists that my fingers started to become numb. I sensed Jones was getting a great deal of satisfaction out of my agony. Several more officers had arrived by this time and Lamont and I were shoved down into a couple of chairs and showed the arrest and search warrants. As he read the details of the search warrant I was wondering how did he catch me. I crossed every 't' and dotted every 'i'. I figured it had to have been something Lamont did.

Occasionally I would glance over to Lamont, just waiting for an opportunity to jump up and kick him in his neck for bringing all this shit down on me. Before I had a chance to act, two uniform officers escorted us out of the building and off to jail. The sidewalks were crowded with 'Lookie Lou's' straining their necks to catch a glimpse of the 'Don' and his 'Captain' being loaded into separate squad cars.

Ashes, Ashes, We All Fall Down

It was a short ride from my office to the police station. As Lamont and I were being lead down the hall to the interrogation, or interview rooms, I instructed Lamont not to say a thing until I get a couple of lawyers down here. Once again Lamont and I were ushered into separate rooms.

The officer told me to have a seat at a small wood table with two opposing wooden chairs. I sat there alone in the six by eight room with no windows, just a clock on the wall. After about ten minutes, a stocky middle age Hispanic man entered the room and introduced himself as Detective Rocha. He slapped a note pad and manila file on the table and plopped his heavyset figure into the chair across from me. "Hey Greg, I've been looking forward to meeting you for sometime now," Detective Rocha said sarcastically. I just gave him a blank look back. Detective Rocha continued, "Thanks to you, we just made the biggest bust in the county so far this year." I still didn't respond, or react. After a brief pause, Detective Rocha opened the file on the table in front of him. He said, "Let's see what charges we have against you so far. It says here you're being charged with high tech grand theft. For the 1,358 pagers you stole from Page Net, GTE, and Mobile Com." I felt a sense of relief that I was only being charged with Grand Theft. I knew the number of pagers was actually closer to 5,000 and from at least 7 more companies than he listed. Anyway, a charge of grand theft usually runs no more than $50,000 dollars in bail, which I could easily raise from the $21,000 dollars cash I had left in my office. I was actually starting to feel lucky. Then Detective Rocha said that I was also being charged with making 'Terrorist Threats' which would up the bail another $250,000 dollars. Shit, now I was looking at a bail totaling $300,000 dollars. I had no idea who I supposedly threatened. The bullshit California law of terrorist threats is one of those charges they give us to make sure you don't make bail. They can get you for saying something like, "I'm going to get you for this," whether you meant it or not. I broke my silence when I said "Just book me, I'll be out by dinner." He then fucked up my world when he said, "By the way, your bail is $2 million dollars." My heart dropped as a large grin appeared on his face. He then explained, "I went to the Judge and asked for special circumstances which raised your bail."

I continued to refuse to speak to Detective Rocha until my attorney arrived. Once booked, I started to make some calls. My first call was to my secretary, Madelyn, to retrieve the cash from my office. Madelyn informed me she had seen the cops counting out my cash and placing it in a big envelope. Shit! That meant I would have to stay in jail over the weekend, until my attorney could get the DA to release the cash. That was only the first of my setbacks. The second of my setbacks was my prior attorney Daniel Greenburg was on vacation. His office recommended another lawyer named Randy. He must be pretty good since Greenburg's people recommended him. Yeah, Right! Randy was young and nice. I have no objection to the young part; it was the nice part that I hated. When your fighting for your freedom, you want a Pit Bull in the court room fighting for you, not a Cocker Spaniel.

On the day of my arraignment Randy said he'd received a copy of the property report of the evidence taken from my office by the San Bernardino Police Department. There was no mention of the $21,000 dollars in cash that Madelyn had seen them counting.

The judge presiding over my arraignment was a young attractive bleach blonde who looked more like a model for Playboy than someone who sat in judgment over your future. Judge Wilder called me forward and asked how I plead. "Not Guilty," I responded. Randy then set out to reduce the bail. The Judge said that he had to file a bail motion, and she would hear the motion in due course. With that, Judge Wilder slammed her gavel down, and I was led out of the courtroom and returned to jail on the next bus.

I figured regardless of what the bail was going to be set at, I needed to come up with some cash, and that didn't include the missing $21,000 dollars the cops supposedly never recovered.

My next obstacle to overcome was; the cops had my black address book, which included all the numbers of people whom I could call to bring the bond money to bail me out. Off the top of my head, I knew the numbers of my ex-girlfriend Jynel, who lived out in Colorado. Shortly before we had broken up, I had opened a safety deposit box and placed $500,000 dollars in it for our future together. I had even put her name on the box for just such emergencies as this. When I called Jynel collect (the only way inmates can make out going calls) she refused to accept the charges. At first I thought there had been some sort of mistake on her part, so I dialed the number a second time. Again my call was refused. I thought "what a bitch!" After I brought her a new car and paid for her to finish her education, she had the nerve not accept my call. At one time, this was a woman I was going to spend the rest of my life with.

I was feeling pretty desperate. Jynel was the only person that had access to the safety deposit box. I instructed Randy, my attorney, to call Jynel and explain my predicament, and to offer her $50,000 dollars if she would retrieve my cash in the company of one of my trusted associates. Jynel told Randy, "I'll think about it. And which bank was it?" Does she think I was stupid? Shit, she would keep all the money for herself while I was stuck there in jail. No way could Jynel be trusted at this point.

I thought about calling my mom, or brother, but then decided to reject that idea because I didn't want to get them involved in all this shit. Then I thought about Lisa. Lisa was a terrific lady who I dated a few years back. She was a young and upcoming gynecologist in the valley. We had split up on good terms, and she had even invested money in one of my ventures after our break up. Fortunately, for me, that venture turned out to be profitable for her. Lisa was pleased to hear from me, but was confused as to why I was calling collect. I explained to her my unfortunate situation and she seemed eager to help me out. I told her I needed her to take $200,000 dollars over to Tony, my bail bondsman in Rialto. Lisa said it would take her about three hours to gather up that kind of cash. She assured me that she'd have it to Tony by 4:00 pm. Finally, there was a light at the end of the tunnel.

When Tony arrived at West Valley Detention Center, shortly after 4:30 pm, to post my bond, he was informed that a hold had been placed on me because of a probation violation. I had been on probation for another infraction about two years back, and was within two weeks of getting off when I was arrested this time. Catching a new case while on probation is a violation of that probation. The light at the end of the tunnel just got dimmer. I immediately called Randy at his office to discuss this new hold on me. Randy tried to reassure me that we could have this matter cleared up when we went back to court in a couple of days. "Just sit tight till then," he said. I snapped back at Randy, "It's damn hard to be patient while in lock up 24 hours a day without even a window in the whole damn jail."

Finally the day of my bail hearing arrived. Randy had contacted my Probation Officer, and had a letter stating I had not violated probation unless I pled guilty or was found to be guilty, therefore the hold should be lifted until such a time as I was found guilty. Randy managed to convince the Judge and assistant DA to take the bail hold off. Except, in lieu of the hold, the Judge increased my bail an additional $250,000 dollars for the probation violation charges on top of the $2 million dollars for Grand Theft and Terrorist Threat charges. That was a sizable chunk of change, but Lisa had put up her home along with my house, which was worth $1.1 million dollars. That would be enough collateral for my bond; I knew I could still make bail. My attorney Randy said, to the surprise of everyone, "Mr. Evans is ready to post bail now your honor." The Judge informed us that bail could not be posted at the court, only at jail. Tony headed back to West Valley Detention Center to await my transport on the Sheriff's bus with the current paper work on my bail status. It was early and I had hoped I would be on the 10:00 or 12:30 bus back to jail. Instead, I wasn't sent back until the 5:00 bus. I was pissed and getting very impatient. I just wanted to go home and sleep in my own bed. Tony was there to post bail as soon as the paperwork had switched hands. At 7:00 p.m., the guard informed me that I had an official jail visit. This usually meant it was my attorney or bail bondsman. Sure enough, as I was led handcuffed into the private visiting room, there was Tony, and he wasn't smiling. Tony spoke first, "Have a seat Greg." I asked, "What's the hold up?" Tony said, "you're not going to like what I'm about to say, the Feds have put another hold on your bail and nobody seems to know what for. All I can get out the officers is that they want you bad." By now the tears were welling up in my eyes. I've been through a lot of shit over the years and somehow I've managed to handle it, but how do you handle your freedom being taken away. I returned to my cell and flopped down on my bunk. I began to sink into self-pity. Mom always told me I probably would end up here someday if I didn't change my ways, but at the time, I thought I knew more than she did.

Once again the guard appeared at my cell and said I had visitors. I figured it must be Randy with the news on the Federal hold. Instead of being led by the guards to the official visiting room, I was escorted to a room that said "training room" on the door. The guard motioned for me to go in. Once inside I saw a half a dozen people in suits. I figured they were with the Feds, who had put the hold on me. I thought I was about to be served with an indictment. The scene was like something out of an X-Files episode. Everyone had on dark suits. And they were sitting in various positions around the room. Three of the men identified themselves as being with the FCC. The other two pulled out ID's stating that they were FBI agents with the Industrial Espionage unit. The woman handed me a business card from the United States Attorney's Office. After hearing all that, I was scared shitless. I couldn't figure out why they had called out all the big guns?

One of the FBI agents approached the chair I was seated in. With his hand on my shoulder, he leaned down close to my face and said, "Mr. Evans, what can you tell us about Galaxy V?" I really didn't have a clue what he was talking about. I responded "Galaxy who?" He retorted, "Come on Mr. Evans, don't play stupid with us. You know

Galaxy V, the communication satellite that was disabled, shutting down pagers, cell phones, radio stations and other transmissions for most of yesterday." I felt slightly relieved when he mentioned yesterday. I answered hostilely, "You can't pin that one on me, you know as well as I do I've been locked up here for over a week now." The woman spoke up before I had a chance to finish proclaiming my innocence. "We have information that you received a wire transfer into your Bank of America account last Thursday and another one showed up yesterday, shortly after the satellite went down. The two transfers totaled almost five million dollars and they were both sent from a corporation in Germany. German authorities are looking into the company that wired the money into your account." I told her, "I still don't know what the fuck you're talking about. First of all, I don't know anything about any monies wired into my account, and second of all you know exactly where I was when the transactions took place. Even if I had done some business with the German Corporation, which I hadn't, what makes you think I had anything to do with the satellite going off orbit?" The younger FBI agent responded, "It fits your M.O. You think you can hide behind your so-called business but everyone in this room knows you're nothing but a mercenary with a laptop. We're going to bring you down one of these days, it's just a matter of time."

After hearing that, I told them I didn't want to say anything else, unless my attorney was present. With that, the U.S. Attorney said, "You haven't seen the last of us. Next time, we'll return with an indictment." The deputies then led me back to my cell. I laid on my bunk staring up at the ceiling, pondering, how the hell did that cash end up in my bank account and not in my offshore account. That would be the more logical place if I were going to hide money. I decided to question Lamont about it the next day.

Lamont's dorm was adjacent to mine. I knocked on the common wall and asked an inmate to get Lamont. Talking through the wall I asked Lamont what he knew about the wire transfer. I was careful not to mention the amounts to him. Lamont said, "Yeah, I just forgot to tell you in all the commotion. It was that day you sent me home from work early. Some woman with a heavy accent called the office for you and because you were on another line, the call was transferred over to me. The woman said she had misplaced the transfer information and needed it again. I didn't think anything of it and just gave her the Twism Telecommunication account number at Bank of America. Things were beginning to become clearer.

Then I heard my name being called over the PA system for an official visit. This time it was Randy, my attorney, bringing me copies of discovery and the police report.

Randy also told me the DA's office was thinking abou
bringing up another charge, because I had hit GTE twice
on different occasions. This was news to me. Randy ex
plained that Lamont and this girl named Vate Taylor, had
set up a phony shipping company in Fontana, and man
aged to convince GTE that they needed $50,000 dollars in
pagers and service. And of course dumb ass GTE gave it to
them. Randy assured me that I had nothing to worry abou
since their whole case was against Lamont. Lamont had
placed the order, signed the checks, the contracts, and per
sonally received the delivery of the pagers. Randy said he
was going to argue at the pre-trial that this was a civil mat
ter, not a criminal matter and it should be dismissed.
Randy then said with the utmost confidence, "Then you can
go home."

It took two and a half months of sitting in jail before
our pre-trial date finally arrived. Lamont and I were led
into the court room in our ugly orange jail jumpsuits with
our wrist shackled to our waist, along with our ankles
shackled, causing us to shuffle our feet in order to walk.
The deputies seated us in the empty jury box, while we
waited for our lawyers, the Judge, and DA to take their
places. In the gallery, I caught a glimpse of John King from
GTE Paging, along with two of my ex-employees, Dexter
Garland, and Julia Love. Julia was a fat computer pro

grammer with an offensive odor about her that I can't explain. I guess the best way to describe her would be to say she was a female version of a computer nerd.

Lamont's attorney David Call approached him, and leaned down to whisper in his ear. Lamont was seated next to me so I strained to hear what it was they were saying. Then I saw a smile come over Lamont's face just before his attorney walked back into the judge's chambers.

Lamont refused to make eye contact with me. Instead, he looked back at Dexter, and gave him a thumbs up gesture. I then asked Lamont what his attorney said. Lamont said that they were dropping all charges against him and that he was indeed going home. I assumed the same was true for me. Randy approached the jury box and motioned for me to slide down to the other end of the bench, out of earshot of Lamont. Randy then said, "OK, here's the deal. The judge is willing to let you out tonight on the stipulation that you return in thirty days with a cashier's check for $100,000 dollars. Then you might just get extended probation." I asked Randy, "How come Lamont gets his charges dropped, and I'm still facing them?" In a lowered voice Randy responded, "Your so-called friend over there isn't getting the charges dropped. He just made a deal with the DA to testify against you. The pre-trial has been postponed because I just got a copy of Lamont's statement. He'll be going home today, but has to return to testify against you before his sentencing."

I jumped up and hopped down to Lamont so fast, he didn't have time to get out of the way. I gave the son of a bitch a head butt to the left side of his head and lunged to take a bite out of his left ear just like Tyson did to Holly-field. The lawyers and several bailiffs had to pull me off of Lamont and literally carry me to one of the cells behind the court room, where I waited for the first bus headed back to jail. The Marshals escorted Lamont back in a private car to jail later that afternoon to await his release that night.

Once back at the jail, I let all the inmates in La-mont's dorm know that he had snitched me out. One thing inmates hate worse than a child molester, is a snitch. It really didn't matter because he was not put back into the general population prior to his release that evening.

By the time I got my phone time, Lamont was back out on the streets. I placed one call to an acquaintance of mine who had plenty of connections on the streets. I knew the guards often monitored the phone calls. I encrypted a message telling Max to make a visit to Lamont's mother's apartment where I figured he'd be staying and welcome him home for me. Max is street smart and I didn't have to spell out what I wanted done to Lamont.

When max and a few of his homeboys were pounding on the front door of Lamont's mother's place, the downstairs neighbor came out and said that she'd moved out a week ago and she didn't say where she was moving too. They new Lamont wasn't worth a dime after testifying against me.

I had just about everyone keeping an eye out for Lamont or members of his family. On occasion somebody would catch sight of him driving around, or at a club, but by the time I got a couple of guys to the location, he'd taken off. Lamont knew I was looking for him. He also knew that price he'd have to pay for snitching me out and testifying against me especially for a job I had no part of.

Out of frustration with the inept job Randy was doing, and the constant postponements, I decided to hire new counsel. The word around the jailhouse was that there was a diligent investigator named Dal Hanseth, who worked for a local defense attorney in San Bernardino. The jailhouse gossip had Dal painted as a crusader for the down trodden, who wouldn't rest until he received justice for his clients. After seven months in jail, I was desperate for my freedom once again. Dal has since become more than just an investigator on my case; he has become a trusted friend.

As it turned out, I made my own deal with the prosecutors for a 16-month sentence, of which, I'd only have to serve half the time. I would also get them to run the time consistently with any time the FEDS would give me. This way I would be released immediately from the county jail and sent to the FEDS and would never see the inside of a state penitentiary. It had been seven months since my arrest, and I figured what's one more month after the shit I've been through so far. I just wanted to put this nightmare behind me.

As for Lamont, he never did appear back in court to testify against me, nor did he receive his sentence for his involvement. In fact, no one has seen or heard from him since he missed his court date of December 4, 1998.

At one point the police questioned me about Lamont's disappearance. I told them I didn't give a fuck what happened to that son of a bitch. If I never laid eyes on him again, it would be too soon as far as I was concerned. Then I told the cops they could kiss my ass.

On March 15, 2001, I was driving on the 10 freeway heading back to the office in my new 500SL convertible when I received a call on my hotline cell phone. That's the dirt phone that calls are not traced and the phone is not linked to anyone. When I answered the phone, "What's crackelating?" I then heard a voice that said, "Guess who I just saw?" "Who," I said. Then the voice said "Lamont. He just got out of jail 2 weeks ago. He got three years for not turning his self in after your conviction." This is what I have been waiting 2 ½ years for. I don't drink but I sure was drunk off revenge. I started making calls and putting the word on the street to anyone out there who saw Lamont to call me and I would give them a thousand dollars.

As I pulled up to the office my heart was beating like a drummer in a rock band. This is what I have been waiting for. I asked Lisa, my secretary, to come into my office. I started telling her about Lamont, that he was out of jail now, and how I had people looking for him. She told me to leave it alone. She said I had too much to lose so I should just leave it in the past. "Fuck that! I spent 16 months and 6 days and 55 minutes between the state and FEDS behind a snitch," I told her. She started into her speech when I looked out the window of my office that over looked the parking lot. I said, "Their goes the motha-fucka right there." That's right, Lamont came to find me, but for what? He knows I want him. He knows what's going to happen to him. Is he here to take me out first? I start to remove my two-way pager and cell phone from the clip on my belt. I then took the $3,000 dollars in cash out of my pocket and threw it in a desk along with my car keys. Lisa then said, "Greg, before you go out there maybe he just wants to apologize." Yeah right, I thought. Then out of nowhere, just like in the movies an angel appeared on my shoulder (not literally) and said, "Just listen to what he has to say." Then here came old faithful, you know the one that appears when the angle appears, a devil, demon, or just one of Satan's workers. "Fuck that Greg, he is here to get you. As soon as he sees you he is going to try and kill you." Decisions, decisions, what should I do? I then looked at the pictures on my desk of my two sons and thought, "I'll see what he wants. Besides I can't do anything here at the office in front of everyone. So I went along with Lisa who refused to stay in her office to the reception area.

If you want to know what happens next, log on to: www.hitechhustler.com

The Crips, A Rabbi, And A Snitch

My crimey on my state case was Otto Lamon
Beasley, whom I consider to be the biggest snitch, rat
bitch, punk, dumb ass in the world had a good scam going
on. Otto had a friend that worked in the credit department
at a major car dealership in Los Angles. She would give
Otto the name, social security number, and the driver's li
cense number of people who came into the dealership to
purchase a car. These people had perfect credit. He then
would go to radio shack where he knew a girl named Kim
who sold cellular phones. Air touch cellular was the carrier
and had a special going: Sign up for service and receive a
free Motorola flip phone. Well Otto would fill out the appli
cations with the information he received from his friend at
the car dealership. On one of these occasions he received
information on a Rabbi out of Beverly Hills whose credit
rating was a perfect ten. Otto had Kim turn on 100 phones
under the Rabbi's name. He took the phones to Los Ange
les and sold the phones for $250 dollars per phone to one of
the biggest gangs in Los Angles called the 'Rollin 60's'. The
service for these phones lasted about 60 to 90 days if you
called in and said you sent the payment in the mail. When
the bill didn't get paid it went on the Rabbi's good credit

After doing some research, I found out that Otto had over 600 phones turned on under someone else's name. At $250 dollars a phone with unlimited calling, he made a nice profit.

What They Don't Teach You In

Harvard Business School

On November 19, 1998, I was transferred from Wes
Valley Detention Center to 535 North Alameda Street, Lo:
Angeles California. This was the Metropolitan Detentior
Center. This is where the Feds keep their prisoners whil
they are waiting to go to court or to be transferred to a fed
eral prison. I was now in this building on the sixth floor ir
the south wing. When I was at West Valley I was sur
rounded by low-life criminals who may be looking at twent
to thirty years for robbing a 7-11 for $75 dollars. At MDC i
is a totally different atmosphere. At West Valley the guard:
are assholes and are as crooked as the inmates. The racia
tension in county jail among the inmates would create riot:
every week. You have gang bangers, crack heads, ca
thieves, purse-snatchers, check bouncers, and every othe
common criminal that's in the San Bernardino county jai
system. You couldn't do anything but watch T.V., pla
cards, or fight.

At MDC you are surrounded by some of the most in
telligent, most sophisticated minds in the country. The
may be in here for committing a crime, but they are no
your average criminals. There are inmates in here tha
have PhD's and Master Degrees. In six south alone the av

erage inmate had made $1.7 million dollars off of a crime. Every type of organized crime family is also there. There were Italian Mafia, Russian Mafia, Cuban Mafia, Jamaican Mafia, Nigerian Mafia, Japanese Mafia, and the Chinese Mafia. With all these different cultures and races there wasn't one fight, argument, or any racial tension. Everyone here got along, unlike West Valley. The Feds treat you like a human being. In six south you have so many activities you don't have time for bullshit. We had pool tables, ping-pong, and at least four chess games going on at the same time. We also had a basketball court, weight lifting area, three T.V. rooms with cable, soda machines, candy machines, two microwaves, ice machines, four telephones, and best of all you have rooms not cells. We ate food like pork chops, roast beef, meat loaf, chicken fried steak, hot links, polish sausage, and the list goes on. We had Sony walkmans and wore Reeboks, Nikes, and Converse tennis shoes. The guard (we only had one per wing) brought in movies from Blockbuster video. You are allowed to have contact visits for an hour and fifteen minutes. At West Valley visits are fifteen minutes through a thick glass. Six south reminded me of a college frat house, except there were no women to do panty raids on. If there is anything you want to read the inmates had it there. They had everything including novels by Tom Clancy to John Grimson. At least four U.S.A. Today's, Wall Street Journals, L.A. Times and several foreign newspapers could be found floating around everyday. Magazines you may have never heard of can be found in six south.

The number one thing I liked about six south is the education I received. Stockbrokers, real estate brokers, politicians, bank presidents, and even a college professor from Princeton surrounded me. With contacts like these one could realistically run an international crime ring (not me, of course).

If six south were a University, the following would be the professors:

*<u>Lou</u> - lieutenant in Chinese Mafia; smuggled seventy-nine kilos of heroin; also charged with laundering $70 million dollars.

*<u>Charles Keaton</u> - From the Home Savings and Loan scandal. He was back in for a probation violation.

*<u>Steve Olson</u> - Swindled $20 million dollars by doing a telemarketing scam; sentenced to four years, his wife got one year.

*<u>Heidi Fleiss</u> - Hollywood madam back in on a probation violation.

*<u>Renee Donoyian</u> - Famous ATM scam; set up her ATM machine that never gave you cash after you inserted you card and typed in your pin number. It copied your

ATM number and pin number to another card and withdrew money from your bank. She made $275 thousand dollars a month.

*Suzanne McDugal - Contempt of court for not testifying against president Clinton in the White Water case.

*Cali Carter - Laundered $700 million dollars. The Feds called this particular sting 'Casablanca'.

*Mike Ramsee - Computer hacker and son of a world arms dealer; stole $15 million dollars from a bank.

*Doc - $20 million dollar Medicare fraud.

*Ben - Grandfather of credit card fraud; swindled Visa, MasterCard, and American Express out of $200 million dollars.

*Sirian - Lieutenant in Philippines military; purchased $2 billion dollars worth of military equipment from U.S.A. and sold it to another country.

*Hi-Tec Vietnamese Gang - Robbed computer chip warehouses all around the U.S. and sent them to Asia.

*Princeton Professor - A chemistry professor that the FBI and DEA noted for being the best meth cooker in history.

*Kyle Ogden - President of Flip It Records; charged with money laundering $2 million dollars.

*Benton "Max" Weatherford III - Twenty-eight year old private international banker. He's also my ace boon coon. Government has charged Max for money laundering of $18 million dollars; he will be out in three years, and will work as my right hand man.

The system sends you to jail to be rehabilitated, but do you think that being around people like this 24 hours a day 7 days a week will change a person to be productive in society? If you want a person to change, it must happen within that person. Adding fuel to the fire just makes the fire bigger.

48 Laws Of Power

While sitting in six south, I wrote business plans, comic books, designed web sites on paper, and I even wrote this book. I knew that when I get out things had to change. I had to be totally legit and profitable. I learned that owning and running a publicly traded company is the fastest and most profitable way of building a company. Remember when Amazon.com was trading over $400 dollars a share but the company had not made a profit. What about Bill Gates whose salary was only $600,000 dollars a year but his worth was over $100 billion dollars. It was all because of his stock he owned in a company called Microsoft.

I read a book in MDC called the "48 Laws Of Power". These laws and philosophies come from some of the most powerful Presidents and Chief Executive Officers in the world. I try to follow these rules as much as possible but some times it's hard, but they do work. I want to share these same 48 laws with you.

Law 1

Never Outshine The Master:

Always make those above you feel comfortably superior. In your desire to please or impress them, do not go too far in displaying your talents or you might accomplish the opposite – inspiring fear and insecurity. Make your masters appear more brilliant than they are and you will attain the heights of power.

Law 2

Never Put Too Much Trust In Friends, Learn How To Use Enemies:

Be wary of friends – they will betray you more quickly, for they are easily aroused to envy. They also become spoiled and tyrannical. But hire a former enemy and he will be more loyal than a friend, because he has more to prove. In fact, you have more to fear from friends than from enemies. If you have no enemies, find a way to make them.

Law 3

Conceal Your Intentions:

Keep people off-balance and in the dark by never revealing the purpose behind your actions. If they have no clue what you are up to, they cannot prepare a defense. Guide them far enough down the wrong path, envelop them in enough smoke, and by the time they realize your intentions, it will be too late.

Law 4

Always Say Less Than Necessary:

When you are trying to impress people with word the more you say, the more common you appear, and th less in control. Even if you are saying something banal, will seem original if you make it vague, open-ended, an sphinx like. Powerful people impress and intimidate b saying less. The more you say, the more likely you are t say something foolish.

Law 5

So Much Depends On Reputation-Guard It With Your Life:

Reputation is the cornerstone of power. Throug reputation alone you can intimidate and win; once it slip however, you are vulnerable, and will be attacked on a sides. Make your reputation unassailable. Always be ale to potential attacks and thwart them before they happer Meanwhile, learn to destroy your enemies by opening hole in their own reputations. Then stand aside and let publi opinion hang them.

Law 6

Court Attention At All Cost:

Everything is judged by its appearance. What is no visible, counts for nothing. Never let yourself get lost in th crowd or buried in oblivion. Stand out. Be conspicuous, at all cost. Make yourself a magnet of attention by appearing larger, more colorful, and more mysterious than the bland and timid masses.

Law 7

Get Others To Do The Work For You, But Always Take The Credit:

Use wisdom, knowledge, and legwork of other people to further your own cause. Not only will such assistance save you valuable time and energy, it will give you a godlike aura of efficiency and speed. In the end your helpers will be forgotten and you will be remembered. Never do for yourself what others can do for you.

Law 8

Make Other People Come To You – Use Bait If Necessary:

When you force the other person to act, you are the one in control. It is always better to make your opponent come to you, abandoning his own plans in the process. Lure him with fabulous gains – then attack. You hold the cards.

Law 9

Win Through Your Actions, Never Through Argument:

Any momentary triumph you think you have gained through argument is really a Pyrrhic victory: The resentment and ill you will stir up is stronger and lasts longer than any momentary change of opinion. It is much more powerful to get others to agree with you through your actions, without saying a word. Demonstrate, do not explicate.

Law 10

Infection: Avoid The Unhappy And Unlucky:

You can die from someone else's misery – emotional states are as infectious as diseases. You may feel you are helping the drowning man but you are only precipitating your own disaster. The unfortunate sometimes draws misfortune on himself or herself; they will also draw it on you. Associate with the happy and fortunate instead.

Law 11

Learn To Keep People Dependent On You:

To maintain your independence you want to always be needed and wanted. The more you are relied on, the more freedom you have. Make people depend on you for their happiness and prosperity and you have nothing to fear. Never teach them enough so that they can do without you.

Law 12

Use Selective Honesty And Generosity To Disarm Your Victim:

One sincere and honest move will cover over dozens of dishonest ones. Openhearted gestures of honesty and generosity bring down the guard of even the most suspicious people. Once your selective honesty opens a hole in their armor, you can deceive and manipulate them at will. A timely gift – a Trojan horse – will serve the same purpose.

Law 13

When Asking For Help, Appeal To People's Self-Interest, Never To Their Mercy Or Gratitude:

If you need to turn to an ally for help, do not bother to remind him of your past assistance and good deeds. He will find a way to ignore you. Instead, uncover something in your request, or in your alliance with him, that will benefit him, and emphasize it out of all proportion. He will respond enthusiastically when he sees something to be gained for himself.

Law 14

Pose As A Friend, Work As A Spy:

Knowing about your rival is critical. Use spies to gather valuable information that will keep you a step ahead. Better still: Play the spy yourself. In polite social encounters, learn to probe. Ask indirect questions to get people to reveal their weaknesses and intentions. There is no occasion that is not an opportunity for artful spying.

Law 15

Crush Your Enemy Totally:

All great leaders since Moses have known that a feared enemy must be crushed completely (Sometimes they have learned this the hard way). If one ember is left alight, no matter how dimly it smolders, a fire will eventually break out. More is lost through stopping halfway than through total annihilation: The enemy will recover, and will seek revenge. Crush him, not only in body but also in spirit.

Law 16

Use Absence To Increase Respect And Honor:

Too much circulation makes the price go down: The more you are seen and heard from, the more common you appear. If you are already established in a group, tempo rary withdrawal from it will make you more talked about even more admired. You must learn when to leave. Create value through scarcity.

Law 17

Keep Others In Suspended Terror: Cultivate An Air of Unpredictability:

Humans are creatures of habit with an insatiable need to see familiarity in other people's actions. Your predictability gives them a sense of control. Turn the table: Be deliberately unpredictable. Behavior that seems to have no consistency or purpose will keep them off-balance, and they will wear themselves out trying to explain your moves. Taken to an extreme, this strategy can intimidate and terrorize.

Law 18

Do Not Build Fortresses To Protect Yourself - Isolation Is Dangerous:

The world is dangerous and enemies are everywhere – everyone has to protect themselves. A fortress seems the safest. But isolation exposes you to more dangers than it protects you from – it cuts you off from valuable information, it makes you conspicuous and an easy target. Better to circulate among people, find allies, and mingle. The crowd shields you from your enemies.

Law 19

Know Who You're Dealing With – Do Not Offend The Wrong Person:

There are many different kinds of people in the world, and you can never assume that everyone will react to your strategies in the same way. Deceive or outmaneuver some people and they will spend the rest of their lives seeking revenge. They are wolves in lambs' clothing. Choose your victims and opponents carefully, then – never offend or deceive the wrong person.

Law 20

Do Not Commit To Anyone:

It is the fool who always rushes to take sides. Do not commit to any side or cause but yourself. By maintaining your independence, you become the master of others - playing people against one another, making them pursue you.

Law 21

Play A Sucker To Catch A Sucker – Seem Dumber Than Your Mark:

No one likes feeling stupider than the next person. The trick, then, is to make your victims feel smart - and not

ust smart, but smarter than you are. Once convinced of
his, they will never suspect that you may have ulterior mo-
ives.

Law 22

Use The Surrender Tactic – Transform Weakness Into
Power:

When you are weaker, never fight for honor's sake;
choose surrender instead. Surrender gives you time to recover, time to torment and irritate your conqueror, time to
wait for his power to wane. Do not give him the satisfaction
of fighting and defeating you – surrender first. By turning
the other cheek you infuriate and unsettle him. Make surrender a tool of power.

Law 23

Concentrate Your Forces:

Conserve your forces and energies by keeping them
concentrated at their strongest point. You gain more by
finding a rich mine and mining it deeper but flitting from
one shallow mine to another defeats extensity every time.
When looking for sources of power to elevate you, find the
one key patron, the fat cow that will give you milk for a long
time to come.

Law 24

Play The Perfect Courtier:

The perfect courtier thrives in a world where every thing revolves around power and political dexterity. He ha mastered the art of indirection; he flatters, yields to super ors, and asserts power over others in the most oblique an graceful manner. Learn and apply the laws of courtier shi and there will be no limit to how far you can rise in th court.

Law 25

Re-Create Yourself:

Do not accept the roles that society foists on you. Re-create yourself by forging a new identity, one that commands attention and never bores the audience. Be the master of your own image rather than letting others define it for you. Incorporate dramatic devices into your public gestures and actions – your power will be enhanced and your character will seem larger than life.

Law 26

Keep Your Hands Clean:

You must seem a paragon of civility and efficiency Your hands are never soiled by mistakes and nasty deed

Maintain such a spotless appearance by using others as scapegoats and cat's-paws to disguise your involvement.

Law 27

Play On People's Need To Believe To Create A Cult-Like Following:

People have an overwhelming desire to believe in something. Become the focal point of such desire by offering them a cause, a new faith to follow. Keep your words vague but full of promise; emphasize enthusiasm over rationality and clear thinking. Give your new disciples rituals to perform, ask them to make sacrifices on your behalf. In the absence of organized religion and grand causes, your new belief system will bring you untold power.

Law 28

Enter Action With Boldness:

If you are unsure of a course of action, do not attempt it. Your doubts and hesitations will infect your execution. Timidity is dangerous: Better to enter with boldness. Any mistakes you commit through audacity are easily corrected with more audacity. Everyone admires the bold; no one honors the timid.

Law 29

Plan All The Way To The End:

The ending is everything. Plan all the way to it, tak
ing into account all the possible consequences, obstacles
and twists of fortune that might reverse your hard work
and give the glory to others. By planning to the end you
will not be overwhelmed by circumstances and you will
know when to stop. Gently guide fortune and help deter
mine the future by thinking far ahead.

Law 30

Make Your Accomplishments Seem Effortless:

Your actions must seem natural and executed with
ease. All the toil and practice that go into them, and also
all the clever tricks, must be concealed. When you act, ac
effortlessly, as if you could do much more. Avoid the temp
tation of revealing how hard you work – it only raises ques
tions. Teach no one your tricks or they will be used against
you.

Law 31

Control The Options – Get Others To Play With The Cards
You Deal:

The best deceptions are the ones that seem to give
the other person a choice: Your victims feel they are in con

trol, but are actually your puppets. Give people options that come out in your favor whichever one they choose. Force them to make choices between the lesser of two evils, both of which serve your purpose. Put them on the horns of a dilemma: They are gored wherever they turn.

Law 32

Play To People's Fantasies:

The truth is often avoided because it is ugly and unpleasant. Never appeal to truth and reality unless you are prepared for the anger that comes from disenchantment. Life is so harsh and distressing that people who can manufacture romance or conjure up fantasy are like an oasis in the desert: Everyone flocks to them. There is great power in tapping into the fantasies of the masses.

Law 33

Discover Each Man's Thumbscrew:

Everyone has a weakness, a gap in the castle wall. That weakness is usually insecurity, an uncontrollable emotion or need; it can also be a small secret pleasure. Either way, once found, it is a thumbscrew you can turn to your advantage.

Law 34

Be Royal In Your Own Fashion - Act Like A King To Be Treated Like One:

The way you carry yourself will often determine how you are treated: In the long run, appearing vulgar or common will make people disrespect you. For a king respects himself and inspires the same sentiment in others. By acting regally and confident of your powers, you make yourself seem destined to wear a crown.

Law 35

Master The Art Of Timing:

Never seem to be in a hurry. Hurrying portrays a lack of control over yourself, and over time. Always seem patient, as if you know that everything will come to you eventually. Become a detective of the right moment; sniff out the spirit of the times, the trends that will carry you to power. Learn to stand back when the time is not yet ripe, and to strike fiercely when it has reached fruition.

Law 36

Disdain Things You Cannot Have – Ignoring Them Is The Best Revenge:

By acknowledging a petty problem you give it exis tence and creditability. The more attention you pay an en emy the stronger you make him; and a small mistake is often made worse and more visible when you try to fix it. It is sometimes best to leave things alone. If there is something you want but cannot have, show contempt for it. The less interest you reveal, the more superior you seem.

Law 37

Create Compelling Spectacles:

Striking imagery and grand symbolic gestures create the aura of power-everyone responds to them. Stage 'spectacles' for those around you that are full of arresting visuals and radiant symbol that heighten your presence. Dazzled by appearances, no one will notice what you are really doing.

Law 38

Think As You Like But Behave Like Others:

If you make a show of going against the time, flaunting your unconventional ideas and unorthodox ways, people will think that you only want attention and that you look down upon them. They will find a way to punish you for making them feel inferior. It is far safer to blend in and nurture the common touch. Share your originality with tolerant friends and those who are sure to appreciate your uniqueness.

Law 39

Stir Up Waters To Catch Fish:

Anger and emotion are strategically counterproduc-tive. You must always stay calm it helps you gain a decided advantage. Put your enemies off-balance: Find the link in their vanity through which you can rattle them and you hold the strings.

Law 40

Despise The Free Lunch:

What is offered for free is dangerous – it usually in-volves either a trick or a hidden obligation. What has worth is worth paying for. By paying your own way you stay clear of gratitude, guilt, and deceit. It is also often wise to pay the full price – there are no cutting corners with excellence. Be lavish with your money and keep it circulating for gen-erosity is a sign and a magnet for power.

Law 41

Avoid Stepping Into A Great Man's Shoe's:

What happens first always appears better and more original than what comes after. If you succeed a great man or have a famous parent, you will have to accomplish dou-ble their achievements to outshine them. Do not get lost in their shadow, or stuck in a past not of your own making: Establish your own name and identity by changing course. Slay the overbearing father, disparage his legacy, and gain power by shining in your own way.

Law 42

Strike The Shepard And The Sheep Will Scatter:

Trouble can often be traced to a single strong individual - the stirrer, the arrogant underling, and the one who poisons goodwill. If you allow such people room to operate, others will succumb to their irredeemable. Neutralize their influence by isolating or banishing them. Strike at the source of the trouble and the sheep will scatter.

Law 43

Work On The Hearts And Minds Of Others:

Coercion creates a reaction that will eventually work against you. You must seduce others into wanting to move in your direction. A person you have seduced becomes your loyal pawn. And the way to seduce others is to operate on their individual psychologies and weaknesses. Soften up the resistant by working on their emotions, playing

on what they hold dear and what they fear. Ignore th
hearts and minds of others and they will grow to hate you.

Law 44

Disarm And Infuriate With The Mirror Effect:

The mirror reflects reality, but it is also the perfec
tool for deception: When you mirror your enemies, doin
exactly as they do, they cannot figure out your strategy
The Mirror Effect mocks and humiliates them, making then
overreact. By holding up a mirror to their psyches, you se
duce them with the illusion that you share their values; b
holding up a mirror to their actions, you teach them a les
son. Few can resist the power of the Mirror Effect.

Law 45

Preach The Need For Change, But Never Reform Too Much
At Once:

Everyone understands the need for change in the ab
stract, but on the day-to-day level people are creatures o
habit. Too much innovation is traumatic, and will lead t
revolt. If you are new to a position of power, or an outside
trying to build a power base, make a show of respecting th
old way of doing things. If change is necessary, make it fee
like a gentle improvement on the past.

Law 46

Never Appear Too Perfect:

Appearing better than others is always dangerous, but most dangerous of all is to appear to have no fault or weaknesses. Envy creates silent enemies. It is smart to occasionally display defects, and admit to harmless vices, in order to deflect envy and appear more human and approachable. Only gods and the dead can seem perfect with impurity.

Law 47

Do Not Go Past The Mark You Aimed For; In Victory, Learn When To Stop:

To moment of victory is often the moment of greatest peril. In the heat of victory, arrogance and overconfidence can push you past the goal you had aimed for, and by going too far, you make more enemies than you defeat. Do not allow success to go to your head. There is no substitute for strategy and careful planning. Set a goal, and when you reach it- stop.

Law 48

Assume Formlessness:

By taking a shape, by having a visible plan, you open yourself to attack. Instead of taking a form for your enemy's to grasp, keep yourself adaptable and on the move. Accept the fact that nothing is certain and no law is fixed. The best way to protect yourself is to be as fluid and formless as water; never bet on stability or lasting order. Everything changes.

Hi-Tech Hustler Scrapbook

The stories that you have read in this book may or may not be true or I may have stretch the truth just a little to protect some people. But the contents are real. There is no way on Gods green earth that the law can stop the wave of the next generation of criminals. Behind keyboards thousands of miles away they will be able to penetrate the tall gates, metal buildings, and million dollar security systems we have put up to protect us. They move like James Bond did in the movies, but their call letters will not be 007. Nor will they consist of 1 and 0. No fancy names. Just plane old Mr. Byte and Mrs. Bytes.

I have included some newspaper articles and statistics from various publications to show you that Hi-Tech Hustlers are here.

They're not just men but also women. They're not just black, but white, yellow and brown. We come out of our adolescence, to pillars in our community. Do you remember the chapter read, "Pirates of the Caribbean?" You read about a device I called the Electronic Snitching Device (E-Snitch). Just keep it in mind. If you would like to know more information on hi-tech crimes, log on to www.cybercrimecorp.com.

Former Computer 'hacker' lets businesses access his on-line service

The staff of Enterlink Technology.

Greg Evans, a spirited computer entrepreneur, spent much of his teenage years doing what is now illegal-acessing other people's computers without their permission. He was not alone. Thousands of young people spent their spare time leaving messages or tampering with busineses and government computers through the phone lines.

Today, Greg Evans does just the opposite, he allows hundreds of other people and businesses access to his computer network.

As the founder and president of Enterlink Technology, Evans has made large quantities of information available to the general public. And all for less than expected fee.

Every day, real estate companies, printers, attorneys, schools and scores of other businesses call Enterlink Technology to obtain information on other businesses, credit reports, county statistics and even the weather.

While other similar services like GEnie, Prodigy, and CompuServe exist, Enterlink Technology is unique in many ways. "In addition to the regular services, we provide credit reports, local real estate transactions and even computer private investigations." Evans said.

Enterlink Technology has been serving High Desert Businesses for three years, but the idea began in the already entrepreneurial mind of an adolescent Evans. "When I was in eighth grade I hooked up with Quantum Leap for the Commodore (computer) which was like CompuServe and GEnie, and I was doing my book report on it using its encyclopdia. When I called into that computer I knew right then and there that was what I wanted to do with the rest of my life; own my own online (computer) service and compete against the big boys." Enterlink Technology is the fulfillment of that dream.

Evans chose the High Desert as the place to set up his dream. "I knew I wanted to start my business in the High Desert because the technology wasn't there." Evans said. "There were no local services like it. All the other services required a long distance call and paying (the telephone company's) per minute charges. I didn't just want the guy sitting in his house, I wanted the businesses. I wanted to offer what the bulletin boards could not.

What Evans has provided is what every business needs - information. Businesses that utilize Enterlink Technologies have access to certain county records (like, fictitious business names), mailing lists, stock reports, business news, 100,000 files and programs, and more.

Enterlink Technologies is unique in another way. Subscribers do not need to own a computer to use it. "People can reach us through FAX, voice, or by a phone call," Evans said. "All that people have to do is pick up the phone. Real Estate transactions and credit reports are available in one hour or less, or they're free."

More services are on the way according to Evans. There services will include a business directory, business profiles, and local news.

There are over 1,100 paying subscribers to Enterlink Technology, including approximately 275 businesses. Enterlink has also undertaken an aggressive sales strategy designed to be economical. Home users can sign up for three months by paying a $60 fee, and allows the customer one hour access per day. The $60 one-year rate allows up to four hours per day of use.

Businesses pay $100 per year and are allowed eight hours a day of access.

Interested parties may obtain further information by calling (619) 961-1156

Gregory Evans, center, owner of Enterlink Technology Information Systems in Apple Valley, and systems analysts Jose Gonzalesz, left, and Karl Halford.

Computer wizard develops new services

By JOHN WHITEHAIR
Sun Business Writer JUL 6 1991

SAN BERNARDINO — Many youngsters like to sneak out of school.

But Gregory Evans used to sneak back into junior high school in his Chicago neighborhood after everyone was gone to run programs on a classroom computer.

And his love for learning about computers paid off in a big way.

At 22 years old, he's president and chief executive officer of Enterlink Technology Information System, a growing computer service company based in Apple Valley with sales of more than $20,000 a month.

When he's away from the office, his companions are a battery-operated telephone and a lap-top computer.

The sky's the limit, said Evans, who plans to expand his service beyond its current 10,500 subscribers and become a serious competitor with industry giants such as Prodigy and CompuServe.

"I want to be big. I want to be real big," he said.

One key to his success has been providing new personal computer service features to subscribers, Evans said.

The company's latest development is a service that allows computer users to send a facsimile without the need for a fax machine.

Although hardware is available elsewhere that enables a personal computer to send and receive messages to and from fax machines, Evans said his service will allow users to do it without the hardware.

Incoming messages will appear on a computer screen and can be sent to a printer if a hard copy is needed. Evans said customers can access his service and use it as a conduit to send faxes to others.

The monthly subscription rate will be $15 for individuals and $40 for businesses, Evans said.

"Really, there's no one out there doing strictly electronic mail," he said. "All the big boys, in order to send mail, you have to belong on the system. With us, you don't have to be a member."

Providing subscription computer services for less than others has been a foundation of the company, Evans said.

For example, he said, Enterlink users have the ability to access popular software programs that may be more expensive to purchase.

The company provides many typical computer service features including electronic travel reservations and electronic shopping.

Students in Hesperia schools a using Enterlink to access encyclopedia and dictionary software, Eva said.

Although he had a college sch arship, Evans left Chicago with $ in his pocket and a big stack of co puter hardware under his arm, a headed for Apple Valley where had friends.

He worked in a computer sto selling computers, and more imp tantly, making contacts with co puter users and owners.

During that time Enterlink established as a computer users' b letin board where computer u swapped information on an infor basis.

But seeing that people would for the service, he turned it in business.

DAVID CREAMER/The Sun

g Evans, president of San Bernardino-based International Communications Brokers, demonstrates
company's 'Ready Cel. The device plugs into a laptop computer and a cellular telephone, enabling
rs to send computer data or faxes from anywhere a cellular phone can be used.

Ready Cel' set for liftoff

A San Bernardino-based
mmunications firm is
out to start
anufacturing a device
at enables laptop
mputers to send data
er cellular phones.

JOHN WHITEHAIR
Business Writer

A new onramp to the Infor-
tion Superhighway is open-
in San Bernardino.

International Communica-
ns Brokers Inc. is moving
o a larger office and man-
acturing complex on South I
reet and expects to hire up to
workers to help with produc-
n of a device that allows lap-
p computers to work as mo-
e communicators.

Gregory Evans, president
d chief executive officer of
e 3-year-old company, said
oduction on the company's
eady Cel" will begin next
nth.

Ready Cel plugs into a lap-
p computer and a cellular
ephone enabling users to
nd computer data or faxes
om anywhere a cellular phone
n be used, Evans said.

Most computers can do
ose same functions using a
andard telephone, but with
e Ready Cel adapter, a cellu-
r phone can be used to trans-
t data.

Manufacturing Ready Cell

TECHNOLOGY

will be the newest branch of the
quickly growing communications and computer company.
Existing operations include:
■ **Telecom Library.** A library
of training and service videos
for communications techni-
cians that are mailed out na-
tionally. Subjects include service and training for computer
networks, satellite and telephone communications.
■ **Prepaid calling cards.** The
cards are sold in stores and allow the use of public phones
without coins.
■ **Pay phones.** Installation and
service of pay telephones,
along with seminars on how to
get into the business.
■ **Pay-per-call** companies.
Training on how to start a 900
telephone business.

Evans formerly owned In-
terlink, an Apple Valley-based
subscription computer information firm.

"I said forget just the computer part of it, I went into everything," he said. "I'm trying
to get into every aspect of communications."

Evans said his company's
expansion includes a computer
laboratory where firms can try
out computer networks before
they purchase one.

The facility also will have a
studio where Evans will produce the company's television
commercials to air on cable

and wireless television chan-
nels.

Allan J. Arlow, president of
the Washington, D.C.-based
Computer & Communications
Industry Association, said the
sector's growth is phenomenal
and will continue to expand as
the Information Superhighway
develops.

"The growth of the computer industry is very rapid," he
said. "Most of the growth will
be in the Information Superhighway."

Jack Kyser, chief econo-
mist, Economic Development
Corp. of Los Angeles County,
said smaller companies, those
with 50 to 500 workers, are
providing much of the Southland's job growth.

"This is where I think
you're going to see the largest
growth," he said. "It's going to
be the small to medium companies."

Kyser said that many com-
munities are seeking companies such as International Communications Brokers that don't
have smoke stacks or produce
hazardous byproducts.

'I think there's a lot of potential for this

ABOVE: Greg Evans, right, research and development director for the Cyber Group Network discusses the company's E-Snitch computer tracking device with Randy Morris, left, the company's software engineer, at a press conference on Thursday. **BELOW:** A prototype for E-Snitch, a tracking device for stolen computes, will allow individuals to download files and destroy them off the hard drive.

Device to protect data and computers

By Dan Evans
Staff Writer

It's called an E-Snitch device, but it might as well be called the LoJack of computers.

The Cyber Group Network Corp., a San Bernardino-based high-technology company, made its first public demonstration on Thursday for a device that can track down a lost or stolen computer.

"I think there's a lot of potential for this," said Troy Cook, a detective with the San Bernardino County Sheriff's Department. "This is a very good idea."

Thursday proved it wasn't just a good idea, but an idea with technology that worked.

In a Webcast press conference, the Cyber Group Network showed how its E-Snitch prototype tracked a computer in real time through the use of global positioned satelites.

E-Snitch also downloaded a file off the laptop computer taken out in a moving car, and then was able to destroy the file off the hard drive of the computer, which was driven

about two miles from the press conference site. Maybe best of all, the device doesn't have to be connected to any land line to be activated.

"This is like Apple Computers," said Greg Evans, the chief research and development for the Cyber Group. "We're about to make history."

What makes the company confident about the success of its product and the software developed for it is that more than $1.9 billion worth of computers were reported stolen last year, according to figures by Safeware Loss Studie

High-tech crime has become such a big topic in San Bernardino County, th sheriff's department started an investigative unit in December, Cook said.

"You're constantly trying to stay up with security for crime prevention," he said. "This is the only product of its kind I've seen."

Device

Continued from D1

The Cyber Group Network which is headquartered at 720 E Carnegie Drive in San Bernardino, is planning on beginning sales of E-Snitch in the first quarter of 2001.

But prices and how the company plan to retail the device -- either thrsough a manufacturer, licensing or its own distribution -- were not plans the Cyber Group Network was ready to divulge on Thursday.

One reason: It is taking the device to the Comdex Fall 2000 information technology conference in Las Vegas next week.

There, it plans to meet with computer manufacturers and government agencies to talk about development plans for the device, said Nisha Kapoor, public and investment relations director.

"We're hearing from a lot of people, but we can't say anything right now," she said

E-Snitch is about six-inches long by four-inches wide. The device will be manufactured to be imbedded into computers, Evans said, so it won't be easily removed from the computers.

In addition to its tracking, downloading and file-killing ablilities, the device also sends out a piercing sound when activated and provide wireless e-mail

The company, which is publicly trade over-the-counter (stock symbol:CGPN), has become a hotly trade stock, even though it closed at just 48 cents a share.

On Thursday, it had a trade volume of 3.88 million shares. In comparison, high-tech stocks Amazon.com traded 7.16 million shares and Qualcomm 9.7 million shares.

"We're up there with the big guys in volume," Evans said. "People are starting to find out about us."

Keeping a rein on CYBER SECURITY

Staff photos by ROBERT A. WHITEHEAD

Gregory D. Evans, 31, is chief strategic officer of The Cyber Group Network Corporation. The company has released software called Hi-Tech Hustler, which teaches consumers how online criminals operate.

Colton company aims for top of its field

By DAN EVANS
Staff Writer

Growing up on the East Coast, Greg Evans never had dreams of pursuing the traditional careers most kids envision like being a fireman, doctor or professional athlete.

"From the time I was 10 years old, I wanted to own my own phone company," he said. "I've always been fascinated with telecommunications."

Now 31, Evans is no Pa Bell, but he has helped start his own telecommunications company.

As chief strategic officer for The Cyber Group Network Corporation based in Colton, Evans is hoping the company

becomes the leading name in computer security.

"When I ask you to name the top bookseller on the Internet, who do you think of?" he asked. "Amazon.com.

"When I ask you to name the top search engine, who do you think of? Yahoo.

"When I ask you to think of the top computer security business, who comes to mind? Nobody. Ask that question a year from now and we hope to be the answer to that question."

Since its startup about three months ago, The Cyber Group Network Corporation is developing computer security technology and is seeking to acquire other similar businesses

See CYBER/C9

Development software technician Maria Diego, 40, works on testing files at the Colton office on Thursday.

Cyber

Continued from C12

and products.

In June, the company released its first product called Hi-Tech Hustler software, which teaches consumers about how high-tech criminals operate. The software focuses on ways to combat data theft, unauthorized computer network access, cell phone cloning and virus exposure.

Hi-Tech Hustler, which is available on CD-ROM, retails for $69.95, and the company met its goal of distributing 20,000 copies of program in July, said

Nisha Kapoor, director of public relations for The Cyber Group.

"What's unique about Hi-Tech Hustler is that it educates people about the way hackers think and what they've done," Evans said.

Also in June, The Cyber Group became a publicly traded company (stock symbol: CGPN). It trades over-the-counter, but it eventually wants to be traded on the Nasdaq, Kapoor said. On Friday, it traded at 10 cents per share.

On Monday, Cyber Group launched a computer search engine specific to high-tech crime called Big Target Meta Search Engine, and later this month it

plans to begin televising commercial spots through Adelphia Media and Comcast CableVision.

In early 2001, the company plans to unveil a chip it has developed that tracks stolen computers.

"It's the LoJack of computers," said Kapoor.

The device — being called a C4 Chip — would be installed in personal computers, allowing its owners to track it 24 hours a day, Evans said.

In addition, it would allow owners to retrieve information off its hard drive, even without being connected to the computer. The chip also would have the

ability to destroy the hard drive to keep information from being stolen, Evans said.

The Cyber Group Network is working to form alliances with computer manufacturers to have the device installed in new products. But the company also plans to sell the chip and have it installed for existing computers for about $100.

The computer security industry is booming, according to the Computer Security Institute in San Francisco. In its annual survey on computer security, 90 percent of respondents reported breaches in their computer networks. Of 273 organizations reporting losses in the survey, more than $265 million was lost.

Mountain Wave Inc. — an Internet reporting site on computer security — estimated the industry will have revenues of about $8 billion this year.

Those type of statistics encouraged the Cyber Group to get in the business.

Even though the company is only a couple of months old, it already has 20 employees and has outgrown its facilities on Via Lata Drive in Colton, Kapoor said.

The Cyber Group is looking to move to a location on Hospitality Lane in San Bernardino this summer.

"We have absolutely no room," Kapoor said.

LoJack for computers?

A Web security firm in Colton recently announced it has a solution to the sort of computer theft concerns that recently surfaced at Los Alamos National Laboratory.

Presently called the C-4 Chip, it sounds an awful lot like LoJack for people with tricked-out computers.

According to a press release by Cyber Group Network Corp. (OTC BB: CGPN), the chip enables the company to pinpoint a stolen computer's location globally   hin 5 feet of accuracy.

But it doesn't stop there: Once a user knows where his pilfered hardware is, he can read data off it even if it's not attached to a hard line, download info or make a backup copy of his files — and then destroy the hard drive and motherboard.

Despite the device's "C-4" nickname, an explosion is not involved, assured Gregory Evans, the company's chief strategic officer. He wouldn't elaborate on the means of destruction since patents are still pending on the device.

"We're not blowing it up with sparks and smoke, or turning it into a bomb," he said.

In fact, the C-4 name given in the press release is a joke — the company hasn't yet come up with a proper moniker for the device, which is expected to hit the market early next year, Evans said.

As if the company's press release needed to get any weirder, another Cyber Group office joke somehow slipped into the text: The announcement says the device was developed in a top-secret location identified as 'Area 74,' conjuring images of company officials squaring off against Fox Mulder.

"I'm a little upset now that (the jokes were in the press release," Evans said.

My first impression was that the device would raise more security issues than i solved: After all, doesn't this mean some one else can remotely access my compute and destroy its motherboard?

Evans says it doesn't. The owner of th computer determines the activation cod for the C-4 chip, and doesn't share it wit Cyber Group unless he needs to have hi computer tracked or fried. And Cybe Group takes its own steps to ensure th person giving them the activation code the owner, not a miscreant. ■

Gray Scott, who is not putting his money where his mouth is, can be reeche at (909) 980-7330, ext. 26, or by e-mail grays@pe.net

THE CYBERSCARE OF '99

By **WILLIAM GREIDER**

Will **AMERICA'S NEXT WAR** be fought on the Internet? The White

House thinks so and is preparing to spend billions protecting

cyberspace from attack. The first casualty will be your privacy

ORGET THE RECENT BANG-bang in the Balkans. The Clinton White House is busy mobilizing its national-security agencies, local governments and key sectors of private industry for a new conflict - a born-again Cold War. The adversaries this time are our unseen enemies in cyberspace.

Instead of Soviet agents, Washington intends to sniff out and disarm malevolent computer geeks - anyone in the vast infosphere who intends to do virtual evil via the Internet. These are presumed to be terrorists or agents of a foreign power, but some may also be home-grown American hackers (or crackers, as the criminally motivated are now called).

The fear is that computer-launched attacks will set off a cascade of disruptions to vital economic sectors: electric power, telecommunications, banking, commerce. The White House is preparing an overall strategy for protecting "critical infrastructures" - a plan that includes everything from instituting a central attack-monitoring system to upgrading computer-security software and creating an ROTC-like "Cyber-Corps" that recruits college students for federal information-technology jobs in exchange for scholarships.

Could the world's mightiest power be done in by its own thickening reliance on digital technologies? Yes, claims President Clinton. "Where once our opponents relied exclusively on bombs and bullets, hostile powers and terrorists can now turn a laptop computer into a po-

tent weapon," he declared in the plan. Cyberterrorism is the hot anxiety in Washington this summer. Your government is mobilizing to stop it. Except they can't yet prove it exists.

"The vulnerabilities are extreme and significant," intones Richard A. Clarke, Bill Clinton's new terrorism czar. "We need to do something extreme and significant about it."

Clarke, a National Security Council bureaucrat with a reputation for aggressive career building, is explaining this to the United States Internet Council's monthly "infosphere luncheon," held in Washington with a teleconference hookup to Silicon Valley. The audience of high-tech executives and policy wonks peppers him with skeptical questions, but Clarke pushes ahead confidently.

"I'm not talking about fourteen-year-olds having fun," Clarke insists. "I'm talking about an attack on the United States or our critical systems within the United States." He mentions electricity, food distribution, communications, railroads.

"We don't have people in the countryside turning valves or switches anymore," he reminds the audience. "It's all controlled by computer systems now ... and almost every one of the systems I've described is subject to attack. They can, if they know what they're doing, turn out the lights. They can turn off the phones, stop water, stop natural gas or, better yet, cause explosions in the distribution systems. Most of the techniques for doing this are available on the Internet."

A draft "National Plan" for protecting these critical infrastructures, not yet public, bristles with melodrama: "Defending America's cyberspace will require action by all Americans.... There has been – so far – no 'electronic Pearl Harbor' to galvanize public awareness about the need for action."

Are you scared? Or does this sound too much like the plot of a sci-fi movie? There are many good reasons, as we shall see, not to lose sleep over the cyberalarms, but a genuine threat does lurk in this project. When the U.S. government sets out to expand its electronic surveillance, the collateral casualties may include personal freedom and privacy.

Here's the plan. At Clinton's directive, and with an initial budget of $1.5 billion, a far-flung and fiendishly complicated bureaucratic apparatus is being assembled across the federal government to "prepare and prevent, detect and respond." That means linking up advanced computer-security systems for monitoring and surveillance – software and hardware that will unite spooks and spies, cops and private businesses in the same vigilant endeavor.

In the latest draft of the plan, I count-recruited by the White House and federal agencies for "public-private partnerships." Government and business will discreetly share info on who's attacking our computers and how to stop them. To reassure reluctant businesses, CIAO promises to amend laws on antitrust, corporate liability for personal data, trade secrets, freedom of information and other matters.

Now are you scared? Your bank and your phone company, not to mention your credit-card accounts and insurance carriers, already possess volumes of intimate detail from your everyday life – where you go, whom you talk with, what you buy, what you're reading. Now the FBI, assisted by the electronic spies from NSA, wants business to become a watchdog partner.

The White House promises that neither the Fourth Amendment nor any existing civil-liberties laws restricting investigative tactics will be breached. "I'm confident that we can protect the security of computer systems without creating Big Brother or his cybernetic evil twin," Clarke assures the Infosphere luncheon. Many of his listeners are unconvinced.

"This is all exaggerated and the result of people in national security being underemployed," says Derek Leebaert, a

ed two dozen new boxes on the organizational chart. The pinnacle is CIAO – as in *ciao* – or the Critical Infrastructure Assurance Office. Last year's anxiety – germ warfare – is utterly absent from the blueprints, though Clinton claims that's what keeps him awake at night. (These stacks of FOR OFFICIAL USE ONLY documents, by the way, were bootlegged to me the old-fashioned way, not through cyberspace.)

The Central Intelligence Agency and the National Security Agency, the Pentagon's supersecret global eavesdropper, are not supposed to spy on Americans, unless they are suspected spies. But on this project, the CIA and NSA are col

THE PLAN doesn't mention that the U.S. is conducting clandestine cyberattacks of its own.

laborating closely with the FBI. A new computer-security central operation, the National Infrastructure Protection Center, is up and running on the eleventh floor of the J. Edgar Hoover Building.

Furthermore, major industries, from banking and telecommunications to oil-and-gas and transportation, are being defense adviser to the Reagan and Bush administrations whose data-integration company, Linguateq, sells software to the telecom industry. "Clarke was talking about CEOs being on board for his program, but that's entirely mistaken. I talk to CEOs all the time. There is great suspicion among them."

A libertarian spirit rules in high-tech circles, alongside fabulous inventiveness and profit. "They're worried about government intrusion," Leebaert says. "They lived through the history of those things in the Sixties, too. The CIA director says we're at war. It doesn't take too much paranoia to believe that, yes, we could revert back to the bad old days of listening and spying on American citizens."

In fact, Leebaert argues, the threat of rolling disruptions is greatly exaggerated because computer systems in major corporations have largely incompatible software programs and thus aren't as interconnected as Washington assumes.

"As any executive will tell you, the interfaces between computer systems are notoriously chaotic," he says. "For instance, MCI's and Southwest Bell's computers talk to each other only with great difficulty. They're still spending millions of dollars for piecework to make the data compatible. Aren't we somewhat

...ate, anonymous self survive in the knowing ether of cyberspace?

...O ARE THESE BAD GUYS?

...FEW MONTHS AGO, DISGRUN-tled hackers took down the ...FBI's own Web site (and the ...ate's) to retaliate for recent raids ...inst hackers. The Melissa virus dis-...d e-mail servers all over the world, ...ew computer worm invaded lead-...corporations and ate their files.

...college student in Sweden turned ...the 911 emergency phone service in ...en Florida counties. Another hack-...puled up air-traffic control at the ...rcester, Massachusetts, airport. A ...lite failure last year silenced 35 mil-...pagers for a few days. The First ...ional Bank of Chicago saw $70 mil-... withdrawn from customer ac-...nts by bogus computer messages. ...hese and many more episodes sug-... scary possibilities. Some are po-...ially dangerous. Plus, there are ...dreds of thousands of additional ...idents" of what look like comput-...reak-ins. Probably there are mil-...s, since most go unreported or ...undetected. (Most are actually ...ple who forgot their password and ... trying.)

...hat's the broad justification for mo-...zation. There are computer-security ...nerabilities, and they need to be ...d. But lumping together every type ...ttack and breakdown, as the CIAO ...t does, feeds a hysterical reaction re-...mbling the early Cold War years. ... York health officials are worried ...ut terrorists attacking the city's wa-...supply. During the Red scare of the ...s, Leebaert recalls, security checks ...e required for fishing licenses at ... York's reservoirs.

...is true that new technology will al-... amplify aspects of human behav-...—including crime and violence. Of ...se society has to upgrade its de-...es. But the federal government is ...ally playing catch-up with private ...ors like banking that have lived ... these security problems for years ... somehow managed to survive.

...draft of CIAO's plan cites poten-...enemies as "rogue nations, terror-...or criminal cartels." Stewart Baker, ...mer general counsel of the NSA ... now represents major technologi-...companies and banking in their se-...ty hassles with the government, is ...convinced. "I am actually kind of ...ptical about terrorist attacks on ...puter networks, because terrorists ... usually do things only to annoy ...ole," he says. "If you don't get e-mail ...three days or the phone doesn't ...k, you're really annoyed, but it

...onal editor WILLIAM GREIDER
...led Vice President Al Gore in RS 809.

doesn't terrify people or make them focus on the terrorists' demands. What terrorists want is to convince people that a society is no longer work-ing, and it's so threatening there's no choice but to give in."

And CIAO itself included a startling disclaimer in an early draft: "Thus far, no major information-systems attacks by known state-sponsored or non-state organizations or terrorists have oc-curred." That admission disappears from the next draft.

The trashing of Web sites may alarm the targets, but Wayne Madsen, a former Navy intelligence and NSA computer-security expert, calls it merely "electron-ic graffiti." Destructive viruses are a le-gitimate problem, but virus-detection systems are also improving in step. Re-porter John Markoff brilliantly sug-gested in the New York Times that the computer realm, with its technical vul-nerabilities, resembles a complex bio-logical system, like the human body, that's infected by surprising new dis-eases. The biological comparison is more hopeful and probably more accurate than visualizing every type of computer fail-ure as a portent of war or terrorism. Soc-iety can and does learn how to deal with biological illnesses, and that's what the industry experts understand about com-puter security: Something bad happens, you deal with it. The best example is banking and finance.

When the leading banks introduced Web pages as early as 1995, hackers had fun messing them up – changing the posted interest rates for loans and mak-ing other mischief. But that didn't get any of them to the cash drawer. And it didn't last long, because bank security of-ficers promptly patched holes.

"As long as there have been banks, people have been trying to steal money from them," says Kawika Daguio, ex-chief of computer security at the Ameri-can Bankers Association. "As long as there have been computer networks, people have been trying to break into them. Our security people are the most experienced in the world. Because we are such an interesting target, people come after us on a daily basis."

The numbers are staggering. A typical major bank or credit-card firm, Daguio estimates, will see thousands of hits each week – even more than 10,000 – from someone trying to gain unauthorized ac-cess to a money account or the systems controlling cash transfers. Security First Network Bank, the first fully online bank, reported a million such attempts during its first six months of business. Again, most of these are innocuous error, not attempted bank robbery.

Banks have this advantage: Their books must balance at the end of every day. "If there is a hole, we see it right away," Daguio says. "And we are far more paranoid than anyone else."

When people do break through to the Web server, they don't find much of value, Daguio explains, "because the wire systems that move money don't really touch the Internet sys-tems. We have a security system like an onion – a bunch of rings around a small center – so you run into layer over layer over layer of defenses. Let's say you're a hacker who gets through one or two layers out of ten. You're still not anywhere close to the real sys-tems that have the actual capability of moving the money."

Banks do occasionally get robbed through cyberspace. But in Daguio's experience, it's always an insider. "The people whose job it is to move money in a bank are the only ones who can do it – and they are the only ones who steal money," he says. "Quite of-ten, we catch them before they leave the building. Do you realize how em-barrassing that is?"

Daguio is executive vice president of a new trade group, the Financial Infor-mation Protection Association, that hopes to teach banking's superior securi-ty methods to less-well-protected Inter-net businesses and federal agencies. "There are chinks in everyone's armor in small places," he says, "but the im-portant thing to remember is, there are no systemic critical faults."

Those still wishing to worry might focus their anxiety on old-fashioned physical reality. Trains and airplanes crash, refineries blow up. Earthquakes, volcanoes and hurricanes are deadly matters, though no one describes Moth-er Nature as a terrorist.

When the CIA and Treasury De-partment conducted "war games" a few years ago to determine how terrorists might bring down the U.S. financial system, their inquiry concluded that the most effective strategy would be this: Shoot the Federal Reserve chair-man and the Treasury secretary, then blow up ten or fifteen of Wall Street's largest financial institutions with Okla-homa City-size explosions.

That might do it. But is this really a new worry?

THE DIGITAL FISHBOWL

IF YOU SAW WILL SMITH IN Enemy of the State, you got a rough glimpse of a plausible future: real-time surveillance that can track people everywhere and anywhere. It should be technically doable in five or ten years. That's not, I emphasize, what the gov-ernment is proposing to do. But the availability of new spying techniques has a way of overwhelming both law and good intentions.

Federal agents were secretly reading citizens' first-class mail years before Congress made it legal, in 1917. After decades of police wiretapping phones, Congress finally authorized it, with proper search warrants, in 1968. The FBI was doing "black-bag jobs" – bur-glaries to collect evidence and plant bugs, sometimes aimed at civil-rights activists or other political dissidents – long before Congress legitimized the practice in 1978. You don't have to be a paranoid to wonder when and how the new technologies cross the line.

"When you enter the digital world, you are standing in front of a one-way

"IT DOESN'T TAKE TOO MUCH PARANOIA to believe that, yes, we could revert back to the days of the gov-ernment spying on Americans," says a defense adviser.

mirror – a digital fishbowl," Marc Ro-tenberg explains. "What's crucial is your ability to protect your anonymity. If you can keep someone looking through that one-way mirror from knowing who you are, you can walk freely up and down the street."

Encryption helps, but anonymity is shrinking fast. As consumers are begin-ning to grasp, they leave behind a vast trail of personal data after every pur-chase, and the information has been turned into a marketable commodity – sold to other firms that use it to target customers, or perhaps to shun them.

In Japan, cell phones are used to track the precise whereabouts of their users (the software lets you punch in some-one's phone number and gives back his location, even the floor he's on). A loca-tional capacity is coming soon to Amer-ican cell phones by order of the Federal Communications Commission. Before long, as Prudential Securities analyst James Lucier observes, we may all un-wittingly be wearing "digital dog tags."

Is it already too late to worry? Scott McNealy, CEO of Sun Microsystems, brusquely flipped off anyone who re-sists. "You already have zero privacy – get over it," he remarked. Not quite ac-curate, but McNealy has a point.

A firm called Image Data started buying up driver's-license photos from states and building a database of faces protected by this happy-go-lucky, slap-dash system of multiple competing technologies? There's not one overarching architecture that can be destroyed."

Silicon Valley's computer execs are allied in their concerns with civil-liberties advocates like Marc Rotenberg, who heads the Electronic Privacy Information Center in Washington. Rotenberg warns, "What we're seeing is a national-security-state infrastructure left over from the Cold War that is reassembling itself. That's about budgets, staffing levels, legal authority and mission. No one says it is our aim to construct a national surveillance state, but when you look at the plans, the technologies and new correlations, the pieces are there. They're being pulled together like magnets on a board."

READING CIAO'S 127 PAGES OF portentous cyberfears makes one wonder whether the Clinton administration has succumbed to end-of-millennium dread of the future. That seems odd, since Clinton and his sidekick, Al Gore, are such robust champions of high tech's promise. Yet the clear and present danger described in these cyberwar documents seems to be the Internet itself.

In a section titled "The Growing

The issue here is control. The emerging digital world confuses people in authority because it madly disassembles their centralized systems and their confidence that they're on top of things.

"For people involved in the Internet, it's very exciting," says Rotenberg. "For national-security people, it scares the life out of them. It's too much chaos and unpredictability. They think to them-

Structured Threat," the White House plan warns, "Terrorists and extremists already are using the Internet – and even their own Web pages – to communicate, raise funds, recruit and gather intelligence. Global proliferation of computer technology . . . make[s] it possible for terrorists to develop a cyberattack capability without great difficulty."

For that matter, human-rights activists and democratic dissidents, from Serbia to Indonesia and China, are also using the Internet in struggles against repressive regimes.

A CIAO chart tries to quantify the dimensions of the threat: Internet devices accessing the World Wide Web will grow from 32 million in 1996 to 300 million two years from now. The ranks of potential bad guys – "population with skills for a cyberattack" – have swollen worldwide from mere thousands to an estimated 19 million by 2001. That's a lot of geeks to watch.

The plan's wrongheaded title – "Defending America's Cyberspace" – reveals a naive misunderstanding and a sense of the nation under siege. Cyberspace, as any teenage hacker knows, does not belong to America. Its very essence is a virtual reality existing beyond place or national borders.

backdoor key to let investigators decode Internet texts. But industry needs reliable encryption to do business (otherwise trade secrets or credit-card numbers are easily stolen). So private enterprise allied with civil-liberties activists to stuff Clinton and Gore. Congress rejected their proposal.

The new plan, Rotenberg and many others suspect, is really an elaborate

IN JAPAN, cell phones are used to track the whereabouts of their users. This technology is coming to the U.S.

selves, 'We can't control it. But if something goes wrong, we're going to be blamed.' These two very different cultures are in deep conflict: the national-security culture that needs order and control and the ability to respond to crisis, and this high-tech culture that's against government rules and regulation, that is purposely decentralized and thrives on unpredictability."

So far, high-tech culture has trumped the national-security forces. For example, in 1993, Clinton and Gore introduced a Clipper Chip proposal to give law-enforcement and intelligence agencies a

end run designed to solve the encryption problem. The government's overtures to industry might get FBI agents into the back room of private computer systems. Meanwhile, Washington is coaxing or squeezing major information companies – Intel, Microsoft, AT&T, IBM and many others – to help solve the digital blockage facing cops and spies. Some companies are warily cooperating.

In sum, the electronic devices that now seem so liberating may ultimately be ensnaring. The digital revolution poses a serious question: Can the free, t a research grant from the Secret ce). Soon merchants would then le to call up picture IDs to see if really are the owner of the credit Surveillance cameras are now sitous in public places.

eople don't quite get it yet," says hberg. "Right now, you've got a se-guard watching a video monitor in bby of an office building. But soon will be computer files of facial im-and when you walk in, your face instantly scanned by the comput-you'll be recognized by name. All devices can be linked together and police on any given day to spy in ime, whether they're looking for a ve in the subway or whatever."

panding computer power already es investigators to digest huge vol-of data at high speed and thus to much wider net for suspects. Au-David Burnham relates in *Above* sw how a Cincinnati prosecutor ed the phone records of 35 million alls from 800,000 local homes and sesses to find a single former Proc-Gamble employee who had d to a *Wall Street Journal* reporter in Pittsburgh.

companies volunteer their data. the sweep of government surveil-is automatically widened, with-ny warrants from a federal judge. rding to CIAO's blueprint, the "Watch and Warning Unit" oper-under the looser restrictions for gn counterintelligence, not the legal threshold required for wire-ing criminal suspects.

'hat's really scary," Rotenberg "is if the surveillance is indepen-from any specific criminal threat v actual criminal conduct. It allows overnment to imagine the worst-cenario for threats, then grants the and technical ability to counter the , without any of the normal give ake of accountability, like a judge asks what the threat actually is."

plan is not exactly reassuring with the best of intentions," it edes, "technology that protects st intrusions, when cast too broad-ight profile innocent activity. . . . portions of the National Plan . . . open the possibility that personal-y rights may be sacrificed in ex-ge for infrastructure assurance ob-ves." Indeed, an internal memo en in March by Ronald D. Lee, an ate deputy attorney general and r NSA counsel, complained that ueprint's discussion of civil liber-raises more fears than it assuages." e core threat to personal privacy lies "best of breed" security technolo-at CIAO envisions for FIDNET – deral Intrusion Detection Net-Intrusion-detection systems, by nature, can be deployed to read un-

coded e-mail traffic and to trace senders and recipients. Without proper authori-ty, that is against the law.

"A lot of people in intelligence and the military want to use these detection sys-tems basically as Internet monitoring," says Wayne Madsen. "That could mean looking at the contents of electronic mes-sages or the patterns of access to Web sites they're interested in. A lot of inno-cent people could find themselves wind-ing up on lists: You've activated some computer program that says you should be monitored, but you don't even know it, and you have no way to find out."

The government promises not to do this (unless perhaps it really needs to). Digital reality plainly calls for a new pri-vacy bill of rights, like the one proposed by Rep. Edward Markey, D-Mass., a vet-eran defender of individual rights. "Give me five minutes with anyone and I will turn them into a privacy fanatic," he says. He's confident that Congress will stand in the way of outrageous intru-sions, with bipartisan resistance.

But it's not always a matter of law. Typically, in the long history of surveil-lance abuses, the laws are brushed aside when the government gets sufficiently scared by shocking events or by civil un-rest. If Y2K disruptions occur at year's end, the chaos could help build political support for CIAO's grand ambitions.

Meanwhile, there is still the protec-tive barrier of private encryption – the codes that the government can't crack. But the Clinton administration is mak-ing incremental progress on getting around that. "The government has said if you want an export license for strong encryption," Stewart Baker says, "one thing to do is make sure the govern-ment can get into the system. So a number of my clients have agreed to hold a key for access. If presented with a warrant, the company will give the government access."

The Justice Department and NSA, Ronald Lee reported, "are currently meeting regularly with industry to de-velop an encryption policy that protects the important interests of law enforce-ment and national security." He did not supply details.

Intel recently added an identifying code to its chips, and Microsoft has done something similar to its soft-ware programs. In both cases, the companies have valid commercial rea-sons for devising this tracking capa-bility, such as catching the culprits who steal copyright material, music

or films off the Internet. But the tracking devices should also be useful to cops and spies.

"We don't know if there's a link," Marc Rotenberg says. "We met with In-tel on the unique ID numbers, and they said many of our biggest customers thought it would be a good idea. Well, we translate that into the federal gov-ernment. It is the largest customer for computers in the world."

HAS THE CYBERWAR STARTED?

RUSSIA IS CALLING FOR A NEW international treaty to curb info warfare, fearing that a new kind of arms race is imminent. Russians claim that U.S. intelligence sabotaged the former Soviet Union's economy by placing "time bombs" inside comput-ers designed to crash. The Russians are not hallucinating.

In 1981, when French spies discov-ered a Soviet program to copy U.S. technologies, the Reagan administra-tion set in motion a vengeful coun-teroffensive. Modified products like computers were prepared for export,

and the Soviets gobbled them up. Then they broke down.

"Contrived computer chips found their way into Soviet military equip-ment," wrote Gus W. Weiss, who was a National Security Council staffer when he dreamed up the scheme. "Flawed turbines were installed on a gas pipeline, and defective plans dis-rupted the output of chemical plants and a tractor factory. The Pentagon in-troduced misleading information per-tinent to stealth aircraft, space defense and tactical aircraft."

If you believe what you read and hear now, the CIA and perhaps other agen-cies are still playing such games, though the Cold War is long over. "As for offensive actions," Richard Clarke confides to the Infosphere luncheon, "not everything you have heard we have done is not true. I try to stay away from agencies looking at offensive techniques, precisely so I won't know."

The contradiction for America is large and obvious: The U.S. govern-ment is working up a righteous fury to combat cyberterrorism even while it conducts clandestine cyberattacks of its own. Indeed, Washington's heightened alarm about cyberwar may be a case of projecting its own power fantasies onto an unnamed enemy.

CIA Director George Tenet told Congress that his agency deployed cy-

bertactics against drug cartels and ter-rorists, according to the *London Sunday Times*. And it is said that computers were used to disrupt foreign-money transfers from Arab businessmen who were financing suspected terror-ist groups.

In the midst of the Balkan war, *News-week* reported that the president autho-rized a cyberattack on "Slobo" Milose-vic – an attempt to crack into his bank accounts stashed in Greece, Cyprus and Russia. This may be empty hype, since foreign banks are not ignorant of com-puter-security methods. But the impli-cations for global commerce are alarm-ing. Does the United States claim the right to subvert and disrupt internation-al finance, while it preaches greater openness in globalization?

Kawika Daguio and the new finan-cial-protection association were so con-cerned that they issued an immediate denunciation of the cyberstunt, though they aren't convinced it was real.

"This kind of thing damages inno-cent third parties, and it damages con-fidence in the global financial system,"

> ## "I'M SKEPTICAL about terrorist attacks on comput-er networks," says a security expert, "because ter-rorists don't usually do things only to annoy people."

Daguio emphasizes. "It's damned hard to do these things, but even talking about it damages confidence in the banking system, which is almost as bad. If we do it, that invites retaliation and emulation, or others pretending they are playing the same game."

The White House is silent on this particular threat to national security and the global economic system: the U.S. government. It declined com-ment on the *Newsweek* account and others. It also does not comment on the European Parliament's complaints that NSA is still operating a massive Cold War–era electronic-eavesdrop-ping system from Britain, tapping into phone calls and e-mail messages all over Europe.

Europeans suspect that this network is now used for economic espionage. Why else, they ask, would we contin-ue to target our NATO allies now that the Cold War is over? The U.S. gov-ernment, in other words, has a lot of questions to answer about the threats in cyberspace and who exactly is spon-soring cyberterrorism.

"This is just like the invention of the atom bomb," muses Madsen. "At first, scientists and others said atomic power had great potential for benefit-ing mankind. Then the military got hold of it, and we had a nuclear-arms race instead."

Cell Therapy

Industry awareness and government legislation have been putting the squeeze on a juicy illegal business

Street savant Percy "Master P" Miller didn't stray far from reality when he wrote *I Got the Hook Up!* (Miramax/Dimension), his May comedy about cell-phone fraud. Just last year, real-life high-tech hustlers scammed the wireless phone industry out of half a billion dollars—a loss that makes Ma Bell one angry mother.

"I call them *ghetto* businessmen," P says of those who inspired the film. During a cellular-phone interview from Los Angeles, the media mogul's syrupy drawl underscores his point. "They smart. They masterminds. It's just that they doing it the wrong way."

Ever since hackers and phone phreaks started "cloning" cellular units in the late 1980s, the wireless industry has been chasing after a criminal coterie that includes everyone from back-alley salesmen to some of the world's top engineers. Hiding out near freeway overpasses or mingling in cramped business districts, the folks who fuel this underground business use handheld electronic boxes called digital data interceptors to scan radio-wave frequencies—literally grabbing registered cellular-phone code numbers out of the air. These legitimate numbers are then reprogrammed into stolen or new phones using a modified microchip.

"It's just as easy as using a Macintosh computer," says a 21-year-old southern California native who sold fraudulent Motorola flip phones back in the mid-'90s. The former gang member, who says he's had a hand in just about "everything" illegal, got out of the business when criminal competition peaked in L.A. and he realized he was risking arrest out on the streets while his partner—a local college student who assembled the phones—was making th... majority of the profits.

"The college guys do it for the same reasons as the gangsters," he says of people like his computer-friendly cohort. "The clout—to make money the fast way. You want to be the guy that says, 'I can hook you up.'"

Traditionally, law enforcement agencies have neglected those in the upper echelons of the trade, picking off, instead, low-level street salesmen like the characters in P's movie, as well as drug dealers, who use the phones for mobility. These days, though, the feds are playing hardball: President Clinton recently signed legislation that makes the possession of cloning equipment a federal crime punishable by up to 10 years in prison for a first-time offense, regardless of whether or not the equipment was actually used to clone a phone. The legislation comes on the heels of a House bill introduced by Representative Sam Johnson, a Texas

Republican who was billed for more than $6,000 of fraudulent calls after a cloner stole his number. (When cloning occurs, legitimate customers receive the bill for illegal calls. But if the bill doesn't correspond to past usage records, the wireless carrier eventually covers any unauthorized charges.)

The industry itself is fighting back too—with harder-to-clone digital cell phones and new security measures for the 38 million or so existing analog cell-phone subscribers who still use high-risk analog models. "We're battling this twenty-four hours a day," says Tom McClure, director of fraud management at the Washington, D.C.-based lular Telecommunications Industry ciation. "We've got 'em on the run."

Indeed, methods such as "encryp" (scrambling a subscriber's airborn nu cal code), "authentication" (a "call response" system in which legiti cellular phones identify themselves to company base by "answering" a di customized "question" correctly), and gerprinting" (using technology bor from the U.S. military, cellular comp can check a phone's unique frequenc verify whether a call is being placed fr cloned unit) seem to be doing the A few years ago, peddlers of illegal ph could guarantee their customers 30 da unlimited calls on a cloned account. fraud can be detected and stopped amount of time it takes to watch *I G Hook Up!*, and cellular fraud-related have dropped from a high of $710 m in 1996 to $500 million in 1997.

"Everybody was looking for the up," says P of his New Orleans envi few years ago. "But a lot of people do busted for it."

The risk, though, hasn't stoppe hustle entirely. Just a few weeks befo release of *I Got the Hook Up!*, police Oakland, California launched one largest cell-fraud stings in the area's ry. After a month-long investigation suspects were rounded up in alleged nection with multiple cloning opera Authorities say the suspects planned phones at $50 a piece and had stolen 1,500 cellular numbers. GTE Wirele mated that it lost half a million d because of the scams. Such busts a and far between because of the s nature of the crime, which usually re collaboration between wireless carrie local police departments to track.

"It's such a mobile operation," Norbert Chu, the deputy district att handling the recent cases. "One gu wreak havoc."

Still, a combination of federal le tion, lower wireless service rates, an ter antifraud protection has caused techno thugs to rethink their market Silicon Valley, many have shifted fro phone fraud to stealing and reselling sive, easy-to-conceal microprocesso as Pentium chips.

Either way, it looks like crime future will never be the same. "Ever knows," says the So-Cal ex-con, "y stupid motherfucker to go in and bank."

Corey Ta

The Master, talkin' cell-celli, rockin' Pello Pelle

Tech Firm Pay Police Agencies to Fight Cyber Crime

Law enforcement: Intel funds sheriff's unit that chases computer pirates. Some fear conflict of interest.

P.J. HUFFSTUTTER
STAFF WRITER

Wander through the headquarters of the Sacramento County Sheriff Department's high-tech team and see what cops call the "ideal model" for fighting cyber crime in an age of shrinking budgets.

Fluorescent lights cast a jaundiced pall over the worn office cubicles, the frayed fabric pinned in slots with tacks. On each desk sits a computer, confiscated from a crime scene and still sporting an evidence tag. Windbreakers with the team logo are a luxury.

Then there are the things visitors don't see.

Like the $10,000 body wire Intel Corp. bought for the unit to use in undercover stings. Or the corporate jet Hewlett-Packard Co. used to fly officers to Silicon Valley, and the tens of thousands of dollars the computer firm spent for the team's travel expenses—flights, hotels, meals—when a recent case took officers out of town.

Tired of being ripped off by high-tech criminals, some of America's most powerful computer companies are fighting back with a

■ **SECOND OF TWO PARTS**

relatively simple approach: Subsidize the local police.

From inside pilferage and brazen heists to Internet piracy and industrial espionage, digital crime in the United States cost computer hardware and software companies about $3 billion last year.

Authorities, who concede they are barely making a dent in the

Please see CRIME, A16

RICK LOOMIS   Los Angeles Times

Sgt. Don Brister of the San Jose Police Department's high-tech crime squad examines computers in search of evidence of piracy.

CRIME: Tech Firm Support Police

Continued from A16

Oregon's largest high-tech hub, city managers have set aside only 2.7% of the Hillsboro Police Department's annual $9.2-million budget for its seven-person computer crime team.

There's no need to commit more, city officials say, because Intel matches the shortfall: $100,000 a year, which pays the salary of one of the police officers and some expenses, according to a 1996 city memorandum of understanding obtained by The Times. Additionally, Intel purchased one officer's car, and helped pay for the team's offices, computer workstations, telephones and fax machines.

Of all 231 cases Hillsboro's high-tech team has tackled between 1995 and April 30 of this year, about 1% involve Intel in some way. As of April, about one-fifth of the nearly $210 million the unit recovered is tied to Intel complaints.

Police say the grant, which is permitted by Oregon state law, has not swayed their focus. Investigators contribute the case ratio to black-market demand for fake Intel computer chips and the company's size.

"This may not be the ideal way for us to do business, but at least we're trying to do something about these crimes," said Police Sgt. Robinson, whose team includes embers of the FBI and the U.S. Attorney's office. "Without us, the criminals run rampant and impact everyone—the companies and the community," he said.

Intel executives insist that their nontraditional approach" of working with police is legitimate and harmless. It is, they say, merely part of a companywide philosophy invest in the communities where employees live and work—not a means of gaining police protection.

"It'd be dead wrong to criticize the police unless we could make a contribution," said Chuck Mulloy, a corporate spokesman for Intel.

Other cities are modeling their efforts after Hillsboro. Chandler, Ariz., which has several Intel manufacturing and assembly centers, plans to pattern its own nascent computer team after Hillsboro.

Such partnerships can hurt the police if companies stop paying, say critics. That's a concern in Hillsboro, where city officials admit there are no guarantees that the Intel grant won't disappear.

"The police don't want to hear this, but if we lose the Intel grant, we'll default on the high-tech crime unit," said David Lawrence, Hillsboro's assistant city manager. "We'll have to go back to what we had before, which wasn't much."

Inside a bland concrete warehouse on the edge of Sacramento's city limits, the Sacramento Valley Hi-Tech unit is the quintessential modern police model for fighting computer crime. The task force was created in 1995 and draws officers from 16 enforcement agencies.

The team's diverse membership—officers from different jurisdictions who possess varied skills—is the key to its strength.

"These guys have the best reputation among law enforcement," said L.A. County Sheriff's Det. Bembry. "They do amazing things with very few financial resources."

Each agency pays for its officers' salaries, equipment and vehicle. But the departments don't feed into the team's general operating budget, which is zero, said Sgt. Tsuchida, who runs the unit.

By comparison, the department's narcotics team receives at least

$55,000 a year for similar costs.

"We serve at least 50 search warrants a year," Tsuchida said. "We couldn't get the $150 a person to get the training to make sure everyone does it the same way. That's a safety concern."

The financial slack is often covered by local technology companies, which contribute seized assets and occasionally kick in for travel and other expenses, Tsuchida said.

"If the companies don't pay, we can't investigate" some out-of-town cases, said Sacramento County Sheriff's Lt. Jan Hoganson, who commands the unit. "We can't afford it."

Cost was a factor in the recent Hewlett-Packard software theft case, which investigators say has links extending from the Central Valley to Southern California, the Pacific Northwest and Central America.

Bill Conley, president of US Computer Corp. in Redmond, Wash., is one of several people Sacramento's unit arrested in conjunction with the case. The charges, of possessing stolen H-P goods, were later dropped, but Conley insists the case was tainted.

"It was the Hewlett-Packard people—not the Redmond police, not the Sacramento cops—who led the whole thing, who took employees off and threatened to take them to jail," said Conley, 41.

Police, prosecutors and Hewlett-Packard officials scoff at Conley's claim, and cite other types of white-collar crimes, such as insurance fraud, which routinely relies on the private sector for enforcement help. And Sacramento's Hoganson insists his team's focus is unbiased, they say, noting that of the 285 cases the team investigated in 1998, only 16 were tied to companies that are members of the unit's steering committee.

But the California Supreme Court takes the issue seriously. In a 1996 trade secrets case, the court upheld the disqualification of a Santa Cruz County district attorney because the office had accepted more than $13,000 from a Scotts Valley software company, Borland International.

The money was used to hire a computer expert to determine whether a former executive had taken proprietary information to a rival firm, Symantec Corp.

Police and prosecutors say the Hewlett-Packard case is different because the corporation's involvement did not influence their decision to file criminal charges.

"I don't see [it] as a conflict, because you're giving law enforcement the money—not the district attorney's office," said Robert Morgester, a deputy attorney general for the state attorney general's office who helped create and fund the Sacramento team.

California legislators are trying to offset the money pinch, by rolling out a $1.3-million state grant to be divided among three task forces: Sacramento, San Jose and Los Angeles/Orange County. In addition, the governor's office has set aside an additional $1 million for the same purpose.

Investigators say that although the grant helps, it's still not enough.

"That money is already spent on training, hiring new people and getting my guys new computers," Tsuchida said. "We're not breaking any laws now, so why should we change what we're doing?"

Pirates of the High-Tech Age

■ Southern California is now home to a sophisticated breed of criminals who, lured by high profits and low penalties, make and sell counterfeit computer software.

By P.J. HUFFSTUTTER,
TINI TRAN and DAVID REYES
TIMES STAFF WRITERS

Southern California is becoming the national base for counterfeiters who make bogus software that looks so good even computer experts can't tell the difference.

Once a problem confined to Asia and Latin America, high-quality fake CD-ROMs made here are showing up for sale in other countries, on Internet sites and even in some retail stores like Fry's Electronics. Authorities have seized nearly $200 million in counterfeit software in dozens of cases in Southern California over the past three years.

The disks are manufactured by a new breed of multicultural gangs that operate somewhat like legitimate software companies. Lured by high profits and low penalties, these criminals work cooperatively with each other, often "outsourcing" different aspects of the operation to business partners in order to save time and money.

"The irony of all this is the counterfeiters are mimicking us," said Chris Chapin, manager of intellectual property enforcement for video game publisher Electronic Arts Inc. in Redwood City. "They are our worst business rivals."

Feeding off the nation' growing number of PC owner the counterfeiters are supplyin consumers with hot new produ ucts such as video games, ta programs and business tool Software pirates can replicat for as little as 50 cents, disk holding programs that com puter companies price at hun dreds of dollars.

"Look, I can make mor money off this than my lawye can defending me," said on self-described pirate, nick named "hax3rz," who was sel ing illegal copies of top-sellin video games on the Internet. " they want it, I'll sell it."

Southern California "is th capital for pirated [software products in North America said Nancy Anderson, senio attorney for Microsoft Corp. anti-piracy group. "Not Silico Valley. Not New York. N Texas. Not Washington. Here.

High-tech piracy flourishe amid the anonymous industri parks in the San Gabriel Valle cities of Walnut, Diamond Ba City of Industry and Rowlan Heights. Investigators hav raided one business park i Walnut so many times th police have dubbed it "Pirat Cove." But operations are al found elsewhere in the region.

Earlier this year, in wh industry experts describe as th

Please see PIRATES, A2

PIRATES: New Breed of High-Tech Counterfeiters

Continued from A1

nation's largest-ever software counterfeiting bust. Westminster police and the FBI arrested a dozen people and shut down an alleged piracy scheme with $60 million worth of fake Microsoft software sitting on a warehouse floor in the city of Paramount.

Atul Sowmitra Dhurandhar, a 51-year-old native of India, and his wife were accused of money laundering and running the operation that for four years allegedly turned out counterfeit CD-ROMs from plants in three Southern California counties. They pleaded not guilty, and their trial begins in Los Angeles federal court this week.

Like computer executives tapping personal contacts for deals, Atul Dhurandhar allegedly used friends to create a business network: a convicted Chinese counterfeiter, who obtained a commercial CD-ROM replicator to copy the disks; a Mexican national, who is allegedly a Mexicali state judicial police officer, to smuggle product across the border; and another Mexican to hire illegal immigrants to run the CD replicator.

Citing an urgent need to crack down on high-tech crime, the Justice Department, FBI and U.S. Customs announced Friday a joint effort to fight software piracy and the counterfeiting of computer products. Dubbed the Intellectual Property Rights Initiative, the three agencies said they will boost enforcement nationwide, but focus on California, New York, south Florida and Boston.

As police break up the operations, the software industry cannot get the public to support its plight.

There is little widespread sympathy when a corporation such as Microsoft—which is worth more than $500 billion—complains that it loses hundreds of millions of dollars a year to piracy.

The wealthy upper class traditionally is seen by the masses as the enemy, said Robert Kelly, professor of society and criminal justice at the City University of New York. In the past, it was oil barons and railroad tycoons. Today, notes Kelly, Microsoft head Bill Gates is the bad guy.

"Fake software is not seen as a threat to the public good," said Alfred Blumstein, a public policy professor at Carnegie Mellon University.

Despite software companies aggressively lobbying politicians and pending millions of dollars on anti-piracy advertising campaigns, the laws remain relatively soft on counterfeiters. The result: people who pirate millions of dollars worth of software often receive only probation.

"It's cheap, it's easy and there's almost no risk," said Sgt. Marcus Frank of the Westminster Police Department, who lead the Dhurandhar investigation. "If you were a criminal, wouldn't you do it?"

Frank said the Dhurandhar investigation peaked last fall when undercover officers staked out warehouses in Paramount, watching as a stream of truck drivers loaded pallets stacked high with fake Microsoft goods.

BRIAN WALSKI / Los Angeles Times
Arcadia police confiscated cash, counterfeit software and computers after arresting two suspects in an alleged piracy operation.

The ringleaders had allegedly been shipping an estimated 15,000 fake Microsoft disks a month nationwide and overseas. By early February, police and the FBI had enough evidence to get a search warrant and raid the operation.

Officers burst inside a warehouse one rainy afternoon and surprised six workers, who were busy printing counterfeit Microsoft user manuals. Here and at nearby facilities, investigators found top-of-the-line CD-ROM duplication equipment, high-speed printing presses and rows of bookbinding and shrink-wrapping machines.

Piles of phony warranty cards spilled out of nearby crates. Sixty million dollars worth of boxed, shiny silver compact disks, all sporting the Microsoft logo, towered over the officers.

And tucked off in a corner, police say, was the investigative mother lode: files stuffed with Dhurandhar's business documents and checkbooks. The paperwork mapped out an elaborate counterfeiting network, according to police, and gave investigators leads on the scheme's money trail.

Dhurandhar, his wife, Mamta—who faces the same charges as her husband—and their attorneys have declined to discuss the case. Ten other suspects will join them at trial this week.

The Key to Success: Networking

Prosecutors say the Dhurandhar case is a textbook example of a modern software counterfeiting operation, where professional networking is the key to success. Someone knows someone with the machinery to copy the disks. Someone else knows of a print shop owner willing to churn out bogus user manuals.

Police say the players in the Southland's growing software piracy industry range from legitimate shop owners to street thugs to U.S.-based Asian gangs, such as the Wah Ching and Black Dragons, to savvy businessmen of all nationalities willing to run a wide-scale operation.

Instead of a crime "family" with workers of one ethnicity answering to a boss, these software gangs operate as independent agents with no specific loyalties. Where traditional crime outfits work to improve the power and dominance of their family, these alliances of counterfeiters end when the job is done.

"If you're a Crip, you're always a Crip," said Det. Jess Bembry, an expert in Asian organized crime with the Los Angeles Police Department. These cases are different because "if it benefits them [financially], warring groups will stop fighting to make money together."

Like computer executives sealing million-dollar agreements with a handshake, the ancient Chinese rite of *guanxi* (pronounced gwan-shee) is the unspoken social glue that defines interactions in some Asian societies. For legitimate businessmen throughout the world, *guanxi* means a person's social rapport is his key currency in the corporate world.

It also is a philosophy that, say police, allows accused software counterfeiters such as the Dhurandhars to build a large manufacturing enterprise.

Dhurandhar allegedly used several of his businesses, including a Long Beach print shop called Digital Colors, as fronts for the secret operation. Heavily tinted windows shielded the workers and gave no clue as to what was being manufactured inside. By day, the firm was a legitimate printing business, according to court documents. By night, it allegedly was a full-scale counterfeiting and assembly plant.

Digital Colors, according to police investigators and the documents they seized, was one hub in a manufacturing labyrinth. Companies in the San Gabriel Valley handled the assembly work. Distributors in Los Angeles and Westminster hawked the goods, which included French, Portuguese and English versions of such bestsellers as Windows 95 and Windows 98, Microsoft's computer operating systems.

In Long Beach, Digital Colors made the boxes, which were stored in Paramount warehouses, one of which housed a $1.5-million CD-ROM replicator that is as big as a high school classroom.

Finished products allegedly were boxed, shrink-wrapped and sold to mid-level distributors. They, in turn, sold the fakes to other software distributors. Some products were loaded on trucks and hauled across the country, police say.

PIRATES

Continued from A28

Even if the people who made the bogus products are caught, the consequences could be minor. But the downside for consumers could be serious.

Counterfeit software could be a copy of an early—and flawed—version of the real thing. It could include viruses that could destroy a person's computer data. And manufacturers refuse to fix fake goods.

Federal penalties for counterfeiting are relatively low. If convicted, a person can be sent to prison for up to five years for software counterfeiting. But most software pirates avoid serious punishment and usually serve less than three years, according to officials at the U.S. attorney's office.

Though a federal statute—the Digital Millennium Copyright Act—enacted last year allows for more serious financial penalties and jail terms, the law remains relatively untested.

To date, federal and local prosecutors have focused largely on those accused of running major counterfeiting operations and laundering money, such as the Dhurandhars. Federal money laundering charges have a much stronger legal bite—a minimum of 10 years in prison—than counterfeiting, said Assistant U.S. Attorney Larson, who is chief of the department's organized crime strike force in Los Angeles.

"It takes me longer to build a case than the time they end up spending in jail," grumbled Det. Jess Bembry, an expert in Asian crime with the Los Angeles County Sheriff's Department. "It's ridiculous."

Few consumers sympathize when Microsoft or other large software firms complain about counterfeiters. The Redmond, Wash.-based behemoth is the world's most valuable corporation and has continually exceeded Wall Street's profit expectations. Last week, Microsoft said its fiscal fourth-quarter profits jumped 62%, with earnings for the period climbing to a record $2.2 billion.

Microsoft has fought piracy since 1976, when Bill Gates wrote his now-famous "Homebrew" open letter to computer hobbyists. The missive chastised computer users and called them "thieves" for not paying to use the operating software, known as BASIC.

Some critics say that software firms fuel piracy by charging too much for their products, but the companies argue that the prices are set to recoup the costs of developing and marketing new programs and make a profit.

"Counterfeiting is stealing. We don't benefit by it. We don't cause it," said Murphy, the corporate attorney for Microsoft.

There are three categories of software piracy. "Warez" is the Internet underground community where users gather at little-known online trading posts to swap files. In license infringement piracy, an individual or organization loads a software program onto multiple computers and doesn't pay the manufacturer for each installation. Finally, there is counterfeiting—the practice of taking a program, burning a copy of it onto a disk and selling the CD-ROM for a profit.

American willingness to buy counterfeit disks terrifies software firms, which have not convinced the public that downloading a $300 business program is as unethical as stealing a $300 leather coat.

In fact, the lack of public outrage has so emboldened the criminal sector that consumers sometimes shop for counterfeit brands.

Take, for example, the Players, a Malaysian crime syndicate known for making fake console video games. Their products, which are sold throughout Asia and on the Internet, sport a small "Players" logo on the jewel case. This logo also is burned on the game disk itself—often in place of the icon for Sony Corp., the legitimate game publisher.

"When it comes to money, morality gets put aside," said Frank of the Westminster Police Department. "Welcome to the new age of international relations."

Times staff writer Rone Tempest in Hong Kong contributed to this report.

Digital Pirates

Southern California—where the Pacific Rim, an entertainment culture and counterfeit manufacturing intersect—has become a hotbed of high-tech piracy. Music, game, movie and computer software CD-ROMs are all fair game.

SOUTHERN CALIFORNIA PRODUCTION NETWORK

Some illicit production facilities run legal businesses by day, but do pirating at night. San Gabriel Valley is considered the region's "pirates cove," but manufacturing and printing facilities have cropped up in Long Beach, Paramount and Westminster's Little Saigon.

1. CD Replicators
Pirates use optical media machines to copy software

2. Printers
Workers churn out fake manuals and warranty cards

3. Holograms
Lasers imprint reflective images on disks

4. Boxers
Thick paper sheets are printed with box designs and assembled

7. Local Consumer
Goods are sold on the Internet or at small shops locally

SOUTHERN CALIFORNIA

5. Glue Shop
Workers cement together boxes and manuals

6. Packagers
All the pieces are combined and shrink-wrapped

DISTRIBUTION
Illicit software also sent to outlets worldwide

NORTHERN CALIFORNIA

TORONTO

MEXICO

NEW YORK

CENTRAL AMERICA

SOUTH AMERICA

MIAMI

FRANCE/ EUROPE

Graphics reporting by
PJ. HUFFSTUTTER /
Los Angeles Times

PAUL CARBO / Los Angeles Times

Infamous Hacker's Sentencing
Brings Little Comfort to Officials

■ **Technology:** Feds won a key battle against computer crime. But they may be losing the war.

By JUBE SHIVER Jr.

WASHINGTON- The Sentencing in Los Angeles on Monday of Kevin Mitnick, the nation's most notorious computer hacker, for breaking into Sun Microsystems computers would ordinarily be cause for celebration by the federal government.

Officals are still smarting from Mitnick's 1983 efforts to break into the Pentagon's computers.

But federal officals are in no mood to celebrate. It has been 16 years since Mitnick-apparently motivated not by money but by the intellectual thrill of reading highly sensitive information-mocked federal computer security. Yet reeling from a series of recent attacks by hackers officals fear that they are no closer now to solving the problem and may actually be losing the war against computer invasions.

"It's not a matter of if America has an electronic Pearl Harbor." said Rep. Curt Weldon (R-Pa.) chairman of the National Security subcommittee on military research and development. "It's a matter of when."

Attackers Penetrate Federal Web Pages

In the last three months alone anti-government hackers have invaded Web pages maintained by the U.S. Senate, the FBI, the Army, the White House, several Cabinet departments and the Idaho National Engineering and Envirnmental Laboratory, which does work for the Energy Dept..

So far, the attacks-which range from notes posted on the White House Web site making light of President Clinton's involvement with former White House intern Monica S. Lewinsky to more ominous assaults that have caused some temporary shutdowns of Web sites without compromising U.S. security.

But federal cyber-cops suffered another blow last month when the House Appropriations Committee, responding to privacy concerns raised by civil liberties advocates denied the Justice Department's request for a "federal intrusion detection network" to monitor all government computer networks.

Indeed, the 37-year old Mitnick remains one of the few examples of successful government detection and prosecution of a computer criminal. In a decadelong crime spree, the self-taught hacker has faced federal and state charges for attempting to break into dozens of computers at universites and private companies.

Mitnick pleaded guilty in March to five counts of a ferderal indictment charging him with making unauthorized electronic transfers of propriety software. He has spent more than four years in jail.

Mitnick likely will be released to a halfway house for time served by U.S. District Judge Mariana Pfaeizer when his case comes up Monday. What's more, he continues to blast the government for what he calls "verzealous" prosecution. Late last month, for example, his lawyers filed a motion accusing the federal government of inflating the financial damage his crimes caused in a bid to hold a case against him.

The government has has another ag"enda in prosecuting him." said Mitnick's Los Angeles lawyer, Don Randolph. "They are trying to make an example of someone accused of computer break-ins. But I think it is wrong any time the government goes beyond its prosecutorial role."

Aided by the availability of more powerful personal computers and faster Internet connections-and facing government computer staffs depleted by corporate raiders-hackers who run the gamut from teenage vandals to domestic and foreign terrorists are taking aim at subduing the new web war tactics.

One measure, introduced earlier this month by Rep. F. James Sensenbrenner Jr. (R-Wis.) calls for more money to train U.S. computer scientists more secure networking standards and a change in procurement standards to allow

Associated Press

working standards and a change i procurement standards to allow beleaguered government agencies easier access to cutting-edge com putor security technology.

A number of congressional pan als has looked into bolstering gov ernment computer security, inclu ing the House Science subcommi tee on technology. Rep. Constanc A. Morella (R-Md.) who chairs th subcommittee, said last month th "the lack of adequate computer s curity in our federal agencies ha the potential to wreak even mor havoc" than the Year 2000 computer bug.

No one has precise figures on the number of assaults on government computers. And government experts are loath to talk about the problem for fear of en coaraging even more computer break-ins.

While many of the most recer attacks on government comput appeared aimed at embarrassing exasperated law enforcement officers rather than stealing classified or sensitive informati assaults on government Web si nevertheless have grown more aggressive in recent years.

Some experts said that defaci of federal Web sites stem from 12-city FBI investigation of cr card fraud and misuse of pilfer passwords by a group suspecte of illegal hacking. The agency has served 16 search wareants California to Texas. It also has questioned about 20 people, so of them teenage boys thought affiliated with a group know a Global Hell, or gH.

Make Money As A Hi-Tech Hustler

Global Technology Publishing will be releasing "Untold Stories of Hi-Tech Hustlers." If you have ever been involved in any Hi-Tech Crime activities such as Computer Hacking, Cell Phone Cloning, Hi-Tech Espionage, Telephone Phreaking, Virus's, or Worms, you can get paid by telling your story. Log on to: www.hitechhustler.com

Printed in the United States
2596